GRADE 1

Reader's and Writer's Journal
TEACHER'S GUIDE

PEARSON

Glenview, Illinois • Boston, Massachusetts • Chandler, Arizona • Hoboken, New Jersey

PEARSON

ISBN-13: 978-0-328-85163-8
ISBN-10:   0-328-85163-9

5 16

Table of Contents

Name _____

DIRECTIONS Say the word for each picture. Write the letter on the line that spells the first sound in the word.

1. _____ m	2. _____ t
3. _____ s	4. _____ s
5. _____ t	6. _____ m
7. _____ m	8. _____ t

Children apply grade-level phonics and word analysis skills.

Name _____

DIRECTIONS Choose a word from below and draw it in the box. Then write a sentence using the word.

escaped   survived

Responses will vary.

Write in Response to Reading

DIRECTIONS Complete the sentence.
When Stellaluna tries to act like a bird, she feels

Possible responses: sad, clumsy.

Children demonstrate contextual understanding of Benchmark Vocabulary. Children read text closely and use text evidence in their written answers.

Name _____

DIRECTIONS Write all of the uppercase letters of the alphabet on the lines below.

Responses should include all the uppercase letters of the alphabet.

Writing

Think about the story *Stellaluna*. Draw a picture for the beginning, middle, and end parts of the story. Then choose one part and write a sentence about it on the lines below.

Responses should be about an event from the story.

Children practice various conventions of standard English. Children write routinely for a range of tasks, purposes, and audiences.

Name _____

DIRECTIONS Choose a word from below and draw it in the box. Then write a sentence using the word.

grasped   embarrassing   clumsy

```
┌─────────────────────────────────────────┐
│                                           │
│                                           │
│                                           │
│                                           │
│                                           │
└─────────────────────────────────────────┘
```

Responses will vary.

Write in Response to Reading

DIRECTIONS Write your answer on the lines.
What does a real fruit bat do?

Responses will vary but could include that fruit bats fly at night, eat fruit.

Children demonstrate contextual understanding of Benchmark Vocabulary. Children read text closely and use text evidence in their written answers.

Name _____

DIRECTIONS Write all the lowercase letters of the alphabet.

Responses should include all the lowercase letters of the alphabet.

Think about the relationship between Stellaluna and Mother Bat. Draw a picture that shows their relationship. Write a sentence that tells about the relationship on the lines below.

Responses should include how Stellaluna and Mother Bat care a lot about each other.

Children practice various conventions of standard English. Children write routinely for a range of tasks, purposes, and audiences.

Name _____

DIRECTIONS Say the word for each picture.

Write **a** on the line if the word has the same first sound as .

1.	a	2.	a
3.		4.	
5.	a	6.	

Say the word for each picture. Write **a** on the line to complete the word.

7.  s a t

8.  m a t

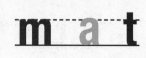 Children apply grade-level phonics and word analysis skills.

Name _____

DIRECTIONS Choose a word from below and draw it in the box. Then write a sentence using the word.

limb   land   perched

Responses will vary.

Write in Response to Reading

Tell something about Mama Bird, Pip, Flitter, Flap, or Stellaluna. Write your answer on the lines below.

Responses will vary but should include something the character says or does.

Children demonstrate contextual understanding of Benchmark Vocabulary. Children read text closely and use text evidence in their written answers.

Name _____

How Polar Bears Hunt

Polar bears live where it is cold. There is ice all around. They have thick fur. They stay warm. They hunt to live. They walk on ice. They look for seals to eat.

Polar bears use clues to hunt. They look for cracks in the ice. Seals swim under water. They come up for air through the cracks. Seals like the sun. They like the heat. Polar bears can find seals in the sun.

Polar bears can slip on the ice. SPLASH! They can fall into the cold water. Polar bears can swim.

Mama bears teach their cubs how to hunt. Cubs learn that hunting is hard work. They must hunt to grow big and strong.

Name _____

Look for Clues

On page 8, circle all the clues that tell about where the polar bears live.

What is it like where polar bears live? Discuss with a partner how the polar bears can live there.

It is cold.

Ask Questions

Write two questions about polar bears.

1. **Responses will vary.**

2. **Responses will vary.**

Make Your Case

On page 8, draw a box around *Mama bears* and underline the words that tell what mother polar bears do for their cubs.

On page 8, find other things that polar bears do. Discuss them with a partner.

Possible responses: They walk on ice. They slip on ice. They fall into the water. They swim.

Children read text closely and use text evidence in their written answers.

Name _____

DIRECTIONS Write your first and last name.

Responses should include
lowercase and uppercase letters.

Think about an interesting event in *Stellaluna*. Write sentences to tell about the event on the lines below. Remember to include details about the characters.

Responses should tell about one
event and include details about
the characters.

Children practice various conventions of standard English. Children write routinely for a range of tasks, purposes, and audiences.

Name _____

DIRECTIONS Draw the word below in the box. Then write a sentence using the word.

brave

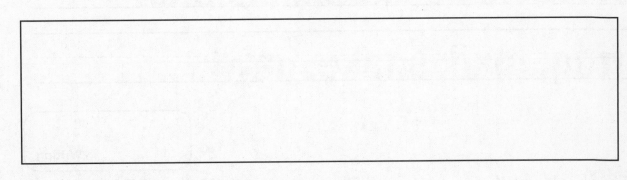

Responses will vary.

Write in Response to Reading

DIRECTIONS Complete each sentence.

Frog and Toad are **friends.**

They want to be **brave.**

Children demonstrate contextual understanding of Benchmark Vocabulary. Children read text closely and use text evidence in their written answers.

Name _____

What kinds of animals did we read about?

Responses should include:
frog, toad, snake, hawk.

Writing

Think about the events in "Dragons and Giants." Pick one event and draw a picture of it. Then write a sentence that tells about the event on the lines below.

Responses should tell about
one event from the story.

Children practice various conventions of standard English. Children write routinely for a range of tasks, purposes, and audiences.

Name _____

DIRECTIONS Choose a word from below and draw it in the box. Then write a sentence using the word.

mountain   snake

[empty box]

_____

Responses will vary.

Write in Response to Reading

Frog and Toad go up a mountain and see a hawk.

I would like to go   Responses will vary.

I would like to see   Responses will vary.

Children demonstrate contextual understanding of Benchmark Vocabulary. Children read text closely and use text evidence in their written answers.

Name _____

Conventions

What do Frog and Toad see in the cave?

snake

Writing

Draw a picture of something Frog and Toad might do together as friends. Then write a sentence that tells about their friendship on the lines below.

Responses will vary but should be about Frog and Toad's friendship.

Children practice various conventions of standard English. Children write routinely for a range of tasks, purposes, and audiences.

Name _____

DIRECTIONS Say the word for each picture. Write the letter on the line that spells the first sound in the word.

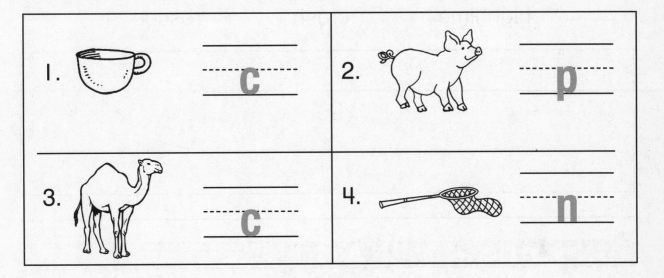

1. _c_

2. _p_

3. _c_

4. _n_

Say the word for each picture. Write the letter on the line that completes each word.

5. ma**p**

6. ca**n**

7. ca**p**

8. ma**n**

Children apply grade-level phonics and word analysis skills.

DIRECTIONS Choose a word from below and draw it in the box. Then write a sentence using the word.

nighttime   crash   rescue

Responses will vary.

Write in Response to Reading

DIRECTIONS Circle the book you like more. Then write a reason why.

I like *Stellaluna* / "Dragons and Giants" more because

Possible response: it is a good
story.

Children demonstrate contextual understanding of Benchmark Vocabulary. Children read text closely and use text evidence in their written answers.

Name _____

DIRECTIONS Circle the words that compare the characters. Then draw a picture to show how the characters are alike.

1. Frog, Toad, and Stellaluna are (animals) people.

2. Frog, Toad, and Stellaluna are (good) bad friends.

Drawings will vary but should include evidence that Frog, Toad, and Stellaluna are alike.

Children analyze and respond to literary texts.

Name _____

What kind of animal is Stellaluna?

bat; Look for evidence of

phonetic spelling.

Writing

Think about an event from *Stellaluna* or "Dragons and Giants." Write what happens on the lines below. Use details.

Responses will vary.

Children practice various conventions of standard English. Children write routinely for a range of tasks, purposes, and audiences.

Name _____

DIRECTIONS Choose a word from below and draw it in the box. Then write a sentence using the word.

clutched   trembling

Responses will vary.

Write in Response to Reading

DIRECTIONS Complete the sentence to tell what happens in *Stellaluna*.

When the owl attacks, Mother Bat _____

Possible response: dodges, shrieks, tries to escape.

Children demonstrate contextual understanding of Benchmark Vocabulary. Children read text closely and use text evidence in their written answers.

Name _____

DIRECTIONS Write interesting words you know or read in *Stellaluna*. Draw a picture for each word.

Responses will vary.	Responses will vary.
Responses will vary.	Responses will vary.

Children analyze and respond to literary texts.

Name _____

DIRECTIONS Circle the complete simple sentence. Write a complete sentence on the line below.

(The birds grew up.)

Stellaluna

Responses will vary but should be a complete sentence.

Draw a picture of one scene from *Stellaluna*. Write details about a character from the scene on the lines below.

Responses will vary.

Children practice various conventions of standard English. Children write routinely for a range of tasks, purposes, and audiences.

Name _____

DIRECTIONS Say the word for each picture.
Write **a** on the line if the word has the same middle sound as .

1. _____

2. _____ **a** _____

3. _____

4. _____ **a** _____

5. _____ **a** _____

6. _____

Say the word for each picture. Write **a** on the line to complete the word.

7.  **c a t**

8.  **p a n**

Children apply grade-level phonics and word analysis skills.

Name _____

DIRECTIONS Choose a word from below and draw it in the box. Then write a sentence using the word.

daybreak   headfirst

Responses will vary.

Write in Response to Reading

DIRECTIONS Draw a picture of where Stellaluna lives.

Pictures should show trees in a forest.

Children demonstrate contextual understanding of Benchmark Vocabulary. Children read text closely and use text evidence in their written answers.

Name _____

DIRECTIONS Add the correct end mark to the sentences.

Bats hang upside down _____

Stellaluna falls into a nest _____

Choose one setting from *Stellaluna*. Draw a picture of it. Then write about the setting on the lines below.

Responses will vary but should be about one setting in *Stellaluna.*

Children practice various conventions of standard English. Children write routinely for a range of tasks, purposes, and audiences.

Name _____

DIRECTIONS Choose a word from below and draw it in the box. Then write a sentence using the word.

obey   rules   behaved

_____

Responses will vary.

Write in Response to Reading

DIRECTIONS Complete the sentence.

I think Mother Bat feels **Possible response: happy**

when she finds Stellaluna.

 Children demonstrate contextual understanding of Benchmark Vocabulary. Children read text closely and use text evidence in their written answers.

Unit 1 • Module A • Lesson 9 • 25

Name _____

DIRECTIONS Add the correct end mark to the sentences.

Do you like bats **?** _____

Can Stellaluna hang by her feet **?** _____

Writing

Draw a picture of one event from *Stellaluna*. Write a sentence about it on the lines below. Be sure to include details.

Responses will vary.

Children practice various conventions of standard English. Children write routinely for a range of tasks, purposes, and audiences.

Name _____

DIRECTIONS Draw the word below in the box. Then write a sentence using the word.

safe

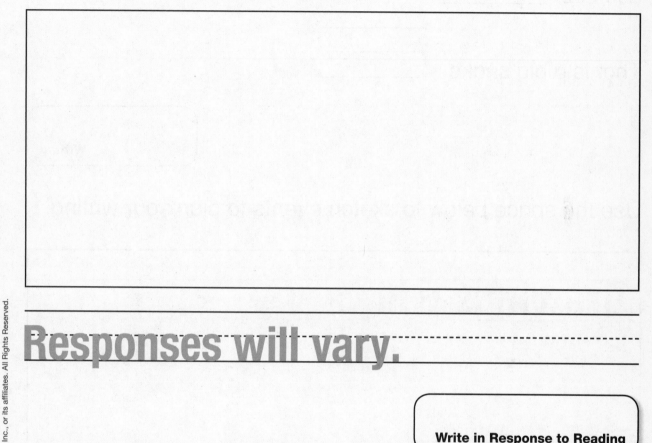

Responses will vary.

Write in Response to Reading

DIRECTIONS Complete each sentence to tell how Frog and Toad feel at the end of the story.

They are Possible response: safe.

They are Possible response: happy.

Children demonstrate contextual understanding of Benchmark Vocabulary. Children read text closely and use text evidence in their written answers.

Name _____

DIRECTIONS Add the correct end mark to the sentences.

Look out ! _____

That is a big snake ! _____

Use the space below to sketch events to plan your writing.

Drawings will vary.

Children practice various conventions of standard English. Children write routinely for a range of tasks, purposes, and audiences.

Name _____

DIRECTIONS Say the word for each picture. Write the letter on the line that spells the first sound in the word.

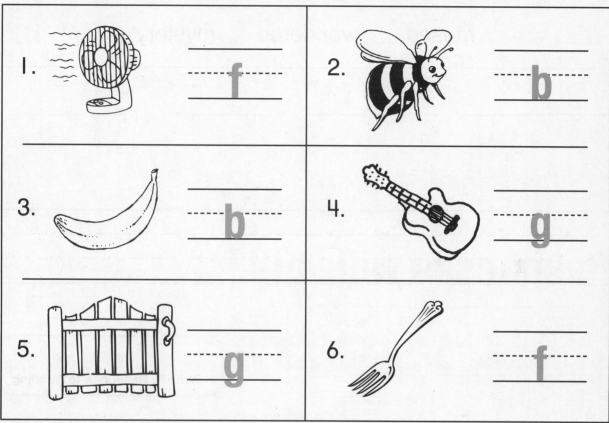

1. _____ f

2. _____ b

3. _____ b

4. _____ g

5. _____ g

6. _____ f

Write two words that rhyme with **gab**.

7. c ab

8. t ab

Children apply grade-level phonics and word analysis skills.

Name _____

DIRECTIONS Choose a word from below and draw it in the box. Then write a sentence using the word.

mused   wondered   mystery

Responses will vary.

Write in Response to Reading

DIRECTIONS Complete the sentence.

People can be different and still be _____

Possible response: friends.

Children demonstrate contextual understanding of Benchmark Vocabulary. Children read text closely and use text evidence in their written answers.

Name _____

DIRECTIONS Write or draw a picture to tell the central message of *Stellaluna*.

How Stellaluna and the birds are alike	How Stellaluna and the birds are different
can fly; perch in trees	birds cannot fly at night but Stellaluna can; birds perch on branches with feet, Stellaluna hangs from the branch by her thumbs; birds sit on top of the branch, Stellaluna hangs below it by her feet

The birds and Stellaluna both feel
confused by how they can be alike and different; care about each other

Central Message of *Stellaluna*
Friends can be different yet alike at the same time.

Children analyze and respond to literary texts.

Name _____

DIRECTIONS Write each sentence correctly.

bats hang upside down.

_____

Bats hang upside down.

The birds and stellaluna are friends.

_____

The birds and Stellaluna are friends.

Use your drawings to write about Frog and Toad's friendship. Write a sentence about each drawing.

_____

Responses will vary but should be about Frog and Toad and the drawings created on p. 28.

Children practice various conventions of standard English. Children write routinely for a range of tasks, purposes, and audiences.

Name _____

DIRECTIONS Draw the word below in the box. Then write a sentence using the word.

together

[ ]

Responses will vary.

Write in Response to Reading

DIRECTIONS Tell about the central message of "Dragons and Giants."

Friends are _____

Possible response: happy when

they are together.

Children demonstrate contextual understanding of Benchmark Vocabulary. Children read text closely and use text evidence in their written answers.

Name _____

DIRECTIONS Circle the complete sentence. Then write your own.

(The snake opens its mouth.)

opens its mouth

_____

Check that sentences are
complete and begin with a
capital letter and end with
a punctuation mark.

Writing

DIRECTIONS Revise and edit your story.

_____

Responses will vary.

_____

_____

_____

_____

Children practice various conventions of standard English. Children write routinely for a range of tasks, purposes, and audiences.

Name _____

DIRECTIONS Say the word for each picture. Write **i** on the line if the word has the same first sound as 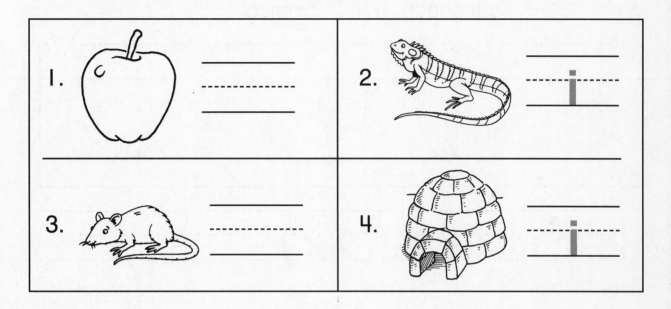 .

1.

2.

3.

4.

Say the word for each picture. Write **i** on the line if the word has the same middle sound as 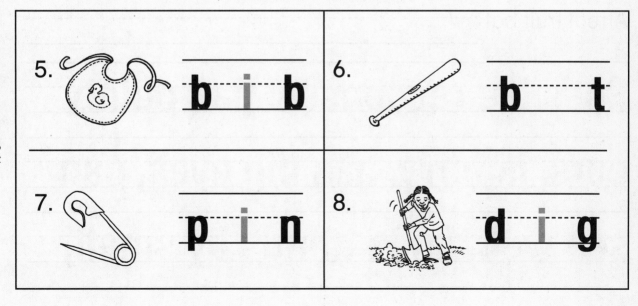 .

5. b i b

6. b _ t

7. p i n

8. d i g

Children apply grade-level phonics and word analysis skills.

Name _____

DIRECTIONS Choose a word from below and draw it in the box. Then write a sentence using the word.

wingspan   tropical

Responses will vary.

DIRECTIONS Complete the sentence.

A real fruit bat

Possible responses: has pointy ears, is furry, has big eyes, can see well, finds things by smell, lives in warm places.

Children demonstrate contextual understanding of Benchmark Vocabulary. Children read text closely and use text evidence in their written answers.

Name _____

A New Family

One March day, Ben and Dad went into the garage. Ben saw something odd. It was high up, on the garage door motor.

"A bird's nest!" Ben cried.

It was made of sticks, grass, and feathers. A mother robin flew out. Dad got a ladder. He saw three tiny blue eggs inside the nest.

"What a funny place for a nest!" Ben said.

"It is warm and safe," Dad said. "We'll park the car outside. We'll leave the garage door open so the robin can get food." Dad moved the car.

Ben checked the nest every day. The mother was often there. After two weeks, the eggs hatched. The tiny birds had no feathers. Every day the mother bird brought worms, and the babies got bigger. Soon they had feathers. One day Ben looked in the nest. The baby birds were gone! Ben was glad he had gotten to know the bird family.

Children read text closely and use text evidence in their written answers.

Look for Clues

Draw your own pictures of bird eggs in a nest, baby birds, and an adult bird. Add arrows to show the order of events.

> **Arrows should show sequence from egg, to baby, to adult.**

Ask Questions

Write a question you have for Ben or Dad about the birds.

Responses will vary.

Make Your Case

On page 37, draw two circles around something you learned from the story.

Responses will vary.

Do you think the story is better with or without the pictures? Tell a partner what you think and why you think so.

Possible response: The story is better with pictures because the pictures add information.

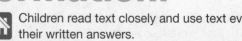
Children read text closely and use text evidence in their written answers.

Name _____

DIRECTIONS Write a sentence that tells something. Then write a question or exclamation. Use a capital letter. Add an end mark.

Responses should be complete sentences with correct end punctuation.

DIRECTIONS Publish your story. Write a title. Draw a picture for the cover.

Responses will vary.

Drawings will vary.

Children practice various conventions of standard English. Children write routinely for a range of tasks, purposes, and audiences.

Name _____

DIRECTIONS Say the word for each picture. Write the letter on the line that spells the first sound in the word.

1. l

2. d

3. h

4. l

5. h

6. d

7. h

8. d

Children apply grade-level phonics and word analysis skills.

Name _____

DIRECTIONS Choose a word from below and draw it in the box. Then write a sentence using the word.

time   sleep

_____

_____

Responses will vary.

_____

Write in Response to Reading

DIRECTIONS Write your answer on the line.
What do ducks do with their legs when they sleep?

_____

Ducks stand on one leg and tuck

the other leg under their feathers.

_____

_____

Children demonstrate contextual understanding of Benchmark Vocabulary. Children read text closely and use text evidence in their written answers.

Name _____

DIRECTIONS Answer the questions. Then write where you found the answers.

1. What animals like to sleep a lot?

_____

Koalas ----------------- and

_____

cats ----------------- like to sleep a lot.

2. I found the answers on pages ___**12**___ and ___**14**___.

3. How do bats sleep?

_____

Bats ----------------- hang

_____

by their **feet** ----------------- .

4. I found the answers on page **4** _____.

Children analyze and respond to informational texts.

DIRECTIONS Circle the nouns. Underline the verbs.

The (duck) <u>swims</u> around.

(Horses) <u>run</u> fast.

The (cat) <u>sleeps</u> quietly.

Writing

Think about two things you learned from *Time to Sleep*. Draw a picture that shows what you learned. Write a sentence that tells about your picture on the lines below.

Responses will vary.

_____

- -

_____

- -

_____

- -

_____

- -

_____

Children practice various conventions of standard English. Children write routinely for a range of tasks, purposes, and audiences.

Name _____

DIRECTIONS Draw the word below in the box. Then write a sentence using the word.

animals

Responses will vary.

DIRECTIONS Complete each sentence using a word from the box.

Ducks	Bats

Ducks _____ sleep on one leg.

Bats _____ sleep upside down.

Children demonstrate contextual understanding of Benchmark Vocabulary. Children read text closely and use text evidence in their written answers.

Name _____

DIRECTIONS Circle the nouns in the sentences below.

(Dolphins) sleep with one (eye) open.

(Koalas) sleep in (trees.)

Writing

DIRECTIONS Write a sentence that tells about a photograph from *Time to Sleep*. Then write a heading.

Responses will vary.

Children practice various conventions of standard English. Children write routinely for a range of tasks, purposes, and audiences.

DIRECTIONS Say the word for each picture.

Write **o** on the line if the word has the same first sound as .

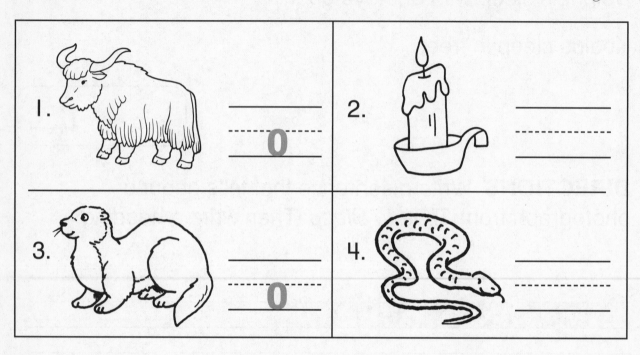

1. _____ **o** _____

2. _____ _____

3. _____ **o** _____

4. _____ _____

Say the word for each picture. Write **o** on the line if the word has the same middle sound as ●.

5. **t o p**

6. **d o ll**

7. **h _ ll**

8. **m o p**

Children apply grade-level phonics and word analysis skills.

Name _____

DIRECTIONS Draw a picture of the word below in the box. Then write a sentence using the word.

sorts

[drawing box]

_____

Responses will vary.

Write in Response to Reading

DIRECTIONS Think about the different ways that people and animals sleep. Write a way that people and animals sleep differently.

Some animals sleep _Possible responses include on one leg, in a tree._

Children demonstrate contextual understanding of Benchmark Vocabulary. Children read text closely and use text evidence in their written answers.

Name _____

DIRECTIONS Draw a picture of the main topic of *Time to Sleep*. Then answer the questions below.

What is the main topic of *Time to Sleep*?

Animals sleep in many different ways.

Retell one detail that supports the main topic.

Responses will vary but could include that some animals sleep in a tree or on one leg.

Children analyze and respond to informational texts.

Name _____

DIRECTIONS Circle the proper nouns. Underline the common nouns.

My <u>dog</u> (Jack) sleeps on the <u>couch</u>.

Many <u>koalas</u> live in (Australia.)

(Henry) enjoys looking at <u>birds</u>.

DIRECTIONS Think of questions you have about the text. Write one of your questions. Then write a sentence to answer the question.

Question: Questions will vary.

Answer: Responses will vary.

Children practice various conventions of standard English. Children write routinely for a range of tasks, purposes, and audiences.

Name _____

DIRECTIONS Choose a word or phrase from below and draw it in the box. Then write a sentence using the word or phrase.

upside down   scared

```
┌─────────────────────────────────────────┐
│                                         │
│                                         │
│                                         │
│                                         │
│                                         │
└─────────────────────────────────────────┘
```

Responses will vary.

Write in Response to Reading

DIRECTIONS Draw a picture to show how bats sleep. Then write a sentence to describe your picture on the lines below.

Responses will vary but should include that bats sleep upside down.

Children demonstrate contextual understanding of Benchmark Vocabulary. Children read text closely and use text evidence in their written answers.

Name _____

DIRECTIONS Circle the verbs in the sentences below.

Birds (sleep) in trees.

Bunnies (hop) with their feet.

Bees (fly) away.

DIRECTIONS Draw two things you learned about how animals sleep. Then write a sentence about one of your drawings on the lines below.

_____

Responses will vary but should include two of the following: bats sleep upside down;

_____

horses sleep standing up; dolphins sleep with one eye open; ducks sleep on one leg;

_____

koalas sleep in trees; cats sleep in many ways and in different places.

_____

_____

_____

_____

Children practice various conventions of standard English. Children write routinely for a range of tasks, purposes, and audiences.

Name _____

DIRECTIONS Draw a picture of the word below in the box. Then write a sentence using the word.

lock

Responses will vary.

Write in Response to Reading

DIRECTIONS Use the word bank to complete the sentences.

| lock their legs   standing up |

Horses can sleep **standing up**.

Horses **lock their legs** so they do not fall over.

Children demonstrate contextual understanding of Benchmark Vocabulary. Children read text closely and use text evidence in their written answers.

Name _____

DIRECTIONS Change the singular nouns to plural nouns by adding an **s**. Rewrite the words on the lines.

cat___**s**___   ___**cats**___

duck___**s**___   ___**ducks**___

Writing

Think about the main topic and key details on pages 6–7 in *Time to Sleep*. Complete the graphic organizer.

Main Idea

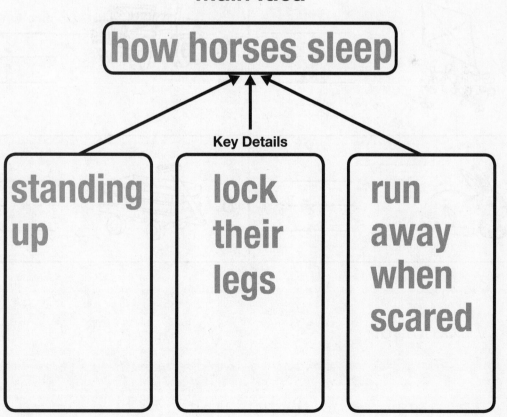

how horses sleep

Key Details

| standing up | lock their legs | run away when scared |

Children practice various conventions of standard English. Children write routinely for a range of tasks, purposes, and audiences.

Name _____

DIRECTIONS Say the word for each picture. Write the letter on the line that spells the first sound in the word.

1. _____ k

2. _____ w

3. _____ j

4. _____ r

5. _____ k

6. _____ j

7. _____ r

8. _____ w

Children apply grade-level phonics and word analysis skills.

Name _____

DIRECTIONS Choose a word from below and draw it in the box. Then write a sentence using the word.

danger   tuck

Responses will vary.

Write in Response to Reading

Why do dolphins sleep with one eye open?

Dolphins sleep with one eye open to see where they are going and look out for danger.

Children demonstrate contextual understanding of Benchmark Vocabulary. Children read text closely and use text evidence in their written answers.

Name _____

DIRECTIONS Circle the verbs that match the nouns.

Dolphins   (look)/looks   out for danger.

A dolphin   look/(looks)   out for danger.

Read your question and think about the answer. Write a sentence that answers the question on the lines below.

Responses will vary.

Children practice various conventions of standard English. Children write routinely for a range of tasks, purposes, and audiences.

Name _____

DIRECTIONS Choose a word from below and draw it in the box. Then write a sentence using the word.

day   high   anywhere

_____

~~Responses will vary.~~ - - - - - - - - - - - - - - - -

Write in Response to Reading

Why do koalas sleep in trees?

_____

~~Koalas feel safe when they are~~ - - - - -

~~up high.~~ -

Children demonstrate contextual understanding of Benchmark Vocabulary. Children read text closely and use text evidence in their written answers.

Name _____

DIRECTIONS Circle the verbs that match the nouns.

A koala live / (lives) in the tree.

Koalas (live) / lives in the tree.

Think about the question your group chose. Then think about the answer your group drew. Write a sentence that tells the answer to the question on the lines below.

Responses will vary.

Children practice various conventions of standard English. Children write routinely for a range of tasks, purposes, and audiences.

Name _____

DIRECTIONS Say the word for each picture. Write **e** on the line if the word has the same first sound as 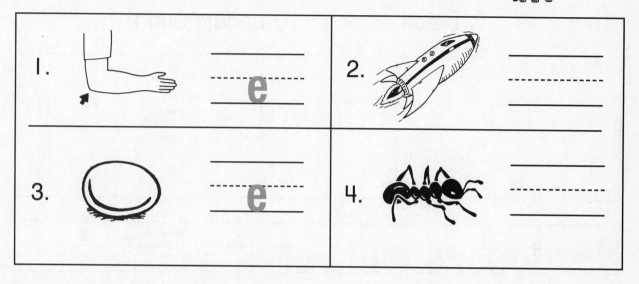 .

1. ----- e

2. _____

3. ----- e

4. _____

Say the word for each picture. Write **e** on the line if the word has the same middle sound as 🔔 .

5. ----- e

6. ----- e

7. _____

8. ----- e

Children apply grade-level phonics and word analysis skills.

Name _____

DIRECTIONS Choose a word from below and draw it in the box. Then write a sentence using the word.

breathe   underground

Responses will vary.

Write in Response to Reading

DIRECTIONS Complete the sentence by using the words in the box.

nose	elephant	bath

If you're an *elephant* _____,

you use your *nose* _____

to give yourself a *bath* _____.

Children demonstrate contextual understanding of Benchmark Vocabulary. Children read text closely and use text evidence in their written answers.

Name _____

A Happy Ending

Once there was a baby bird. He grew up with a family of ducks. He didn't look like them, though. He was fuzzy and gray. The other ducks called him ugly. One day the ducks got a big surprise. The baby bird had grown up. He had turned beautiful. His feathers were as white as snow. He was really a swan!

That is the tale of the ugly duckling. Ducks are different from swans. Grown-up swans often have bright white feathers. They have long, curved necks. Baby swans look different.

A mother swan lays from three to nine eggs. After five weeks, the eggs hatch. A baby swan has gray feathers and a short neck.

Just as in the story, the baby swan has a happy ending. As the baby grows, it changes. After a year, its feathers become white. Its neck gets long. The "ugly" baby becomes a graceful swan!

Children read text closely to determine what the text says.

Name _____

Look for Clues

Draw a picture of a duck and a swan. Draw arrows to show two ways ducks and swans are different.

Possible responses: Arrows might indicate color, size, neck length.

Ask Questions

On page 61, underline a sentence in the text that you would like to know more about.

Responses will vary.

Make Your Case

At the beginning of page 61, draw a box around something you learned from the story about the ugly duckling.

Responses will vary.

Children read text closely to determine what the text says.

Name _____

DIRECTIONS Complete the sentences below by adding a question word at the beginning and a question mark at the end.

| Who | What | When | Where | Why | How |

_____ **When/How** _____ do you get to school **?** _____

_____ **What/Where** _____ is your favorite color **?** _____

Writing

DIRECTIONS Draw one animal from the text. Write a question about the animal. Then write an answer to that question.

Question: **Responses will vary.**

_____

Answer: **Responses will vary.**

_____

Children practice various conventions of standard English. Children write routinely for a range of tasks, purposes, and audiences.

Unit 1 • Module B • Lesson 8 • 63

Name _____

DIRECTIONS Choose a word from below and draw it in the box. Then write a sentence using the word.

hang   high   feet   eyes

Responses will vary.

DIRECTIONS Write your answers on the lines.

What can animals do with their feet?

1. A duck can _sleep on one foot._

2. A water strider can _walk on water._

Children demonstrate contextual understanding of Benchmark Vocabulary. Children read text closely and use text evidence in their written answers.

Lesson 9

Name _____

DIRECTIONS Write the question below correctly.

what do you do with your nose

<u>What do you do with your nose?</u>

DIRECTIONS How do animals use their body parts? Think about what you learned from the texts. Write 2 facts on the lines below.

Fact 1

Responses will vary.

Fact 2

Responses will vary.

Children practice various conventions of standard English. Children write routinely for a range of tasks, purposes, and audiences.

Name _____

DIRECTIONS Choose a word from below and draw it in the box. Then write a sentence using the word.

pesky   warn

Responses will vary.

Write in Response to Reading

DIRECTIONS Write a sentence about how an animal uses its tail.

Responses will vary but should include how a giraffe, skunk, lizard, monkey, or scorpion uses its tail.

Children demonstrate contextual understanding of Benchmark Vocabulary. Children read text closely and use text evidence in their written answers.

Name _____

DIRECTIONS Circle the common nouns. Underline the proper nouns.

(turtle)   Swan Lake   (pencil)   Mr. Smith

New York   May   (cats)   (pool)

Writing

Draw a picture of an animal you will ask a question about. Plan your writing. Write a question about your animal.

Responses will vary.

_____

_____

_____

_____

_____

_____

_____

_____

_____

Children practice various conventions of standard English. Children write routinely for a range of tasks, purposes, and audiences.

Name _____

DIRECTIONS Say the word for each picture. Write the letter or letters on the line that spells the first sound in the word.

1. v

2. z

3. qu

4. z

5. y

6. v

7. qu

8. y

Children apply grade-level phonics and word analysis skills.

Name _____

DIRECTIONS Choose a word from below and draw it in the box. Then write a sentence using the word.

spot   squirt

Responses will vary.

Write in Response to Reading

DIRECTIONS Draw a picture of the answer. Then write the answer on the line below.

What can a lizard do with its tail?

Drawing should show the lizard's tail broken off from its body.

Responses should describe the broken tail.

 Children demonstrate contextual understanding of Benchmark Vocabulary. Children read text closely and use text evidence in their written answers.

Name _____

DIRECTIONS Read the words in the box. Choose the best word to answer the question or complete the sentence.

| bat | giraffe | humpback whale | tail | tree |

1. Which animal brushes flies off with its tail?

giraffe _____

2. What happens after a skunk lifts its _____ **tail** _____ ?
It sprays a stinky spray.

3. How does a _____ **bat** _____ use its ears?
It uses its ears to see.

4. What uses its ears to hear sounds hundreds of miles away?

humpback whale _____

5. Where does a monkey use its tail?

The monkey uses its tail to hang from a _____ **tree** _____.

Children analyze and respond to informational texts.

Name _____

DIRECTIONS Complete the sentence by adding **-s** or **-es** to the action verb.

hunt   An eagle _____ hunts _____ small animals.

catch   A pelican _____ catches _____ fish with its mouth.

Write your question about an animal.

Responses will vary.

Write the answer to your question.

Responses will vary.

Children practice various conventions of standard English. Children write routinely for a range of tasks, purposes, and audiences.

Name _____

DIRECTIONS Choose a word from below and draw it in the box. Then write a sentence using the word.

sticky   scoop   swallow

Responses will vary.

Draw the animal with the most interesting mouth.

Drawings will vary.

Why is this mouth interesting?

Response should support child's choice of animal.

Children demonstrate contextual understanding of Benchmark Vocabulary. Children read text closely and use text evidence in their written answers.

Name _____

DIRECTIONS Draw a picture of a pelican. Show how the pelican eats a fish.

Drawing should show a pelican with its big mouth open wide to scoop up a fish.

Write words or sentences to explain your drawing.

Words and sentences should explain that the pelican uses its mouth as a net to scoop up fish.

Children analyze and respond to informational texts.

Name _____

DIRECTIONS Complete the sentences with **is** or **are**.

A pelican _____**is**_____ a bird.

Chimpanzees _____**are**_____ bigger than geckos.

Writing

DIRECTIONS Write your final question and answer. Use your best handwriting.

Responses will vary but should be a question and answer with no errors.

 Children practice various conventions of standard English. Children write routinely for a range of tasks, purposes, and audiences.

Name _____

DIRECTIONS Say the word for each picture. Write **u** on the line if the word has the same first sound as .

1. _____ u _____

2. _____ _____

3. _____ _____

4. _____ u _____

Say the word for each picture. Write **u** on the line if the word has the same middle sound as 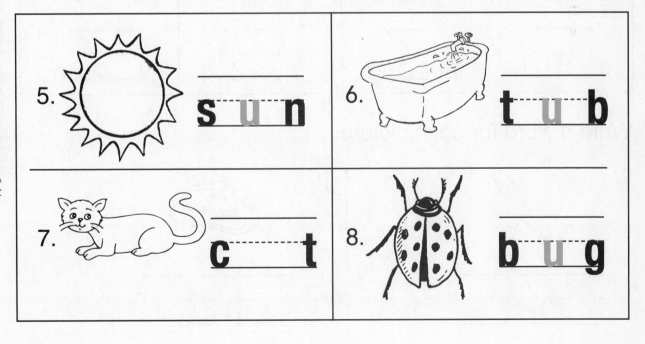.

5. **s u n**

6. **t u b**

7. **c _ t**

8. **b u g**

Children apply grade-level phonics and word analysis skills.

Name _____

DIRECTIONS Say the word for each picture.
Write **a** on the line if you hear the **short a** sound.

c<u>a</u>t

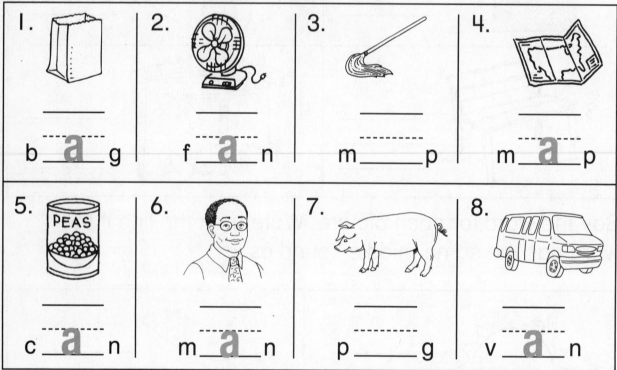

| 1. b _a_ g | 2. f _a_ n | 3. m____p | 4. m _a_ p |
| 5. c _a_ n | 6. m _a_ n | 7. p____g | 8. v _a_ n |

Write a word for each picture.

9.

bat

10.

hat

Children apply grade-level phonics and word analysis skills.

Name _____

DIRECTIONS Choose a word from below and draw it in the box. Then write a sentence using the word.

learning   proud

[box]

Responses will vary. _____

Write in Response to Reading

DIRECTIONS Draw a picture that shows one character, setting, and major event from *A Fine, Fine School.* Then write the character, setting, and event on the lines below.

Character: Possible responses: Mr. Keene, Tillie, Tillie's brother, Beans

Setting: Possible responses: school, school bus, Tillie's house, park

Event: Responses should include an event from the text.

Children demonstrate contextual understanding of Benchmark Vocabulary. Children read closely and use text evidence in their written answers.

DIRECTIONS Rewrite the sentence below correctly.

my three favorite colors are red yellow and blue

My three favorite colors are red, yellow, and blue.

Writing

DIRECTIONS Name the topic. Write one fact and one opinion about Mr. Keene.

Topic: **Mr. Keene**

Fact: Mr. Keene **Possible response: is the principal at the school.**

Opinion: I think Mr. Keene **Possible response: is happy.**

Children practice various conventions of standard English. Children write routinely for a range of tasks, purposes, and audiences.

Name _____

DIRECTIONS Choose a word from below and draw it in the box. Then write a sentence using the word.

strolled   waved

Responses will vary.

DIRECTIONS Write three things Tillie does with her brother.

Possible responses: climb, walk, skip, swing

Children demonstrate contextual understanding of Benchmark Vocabulary. Children read text closely and use text evidence in their written answers.

DIRECTIONS Circle the word that tells what is happening now. Underline the words that tell what will happen. Put an X on the word that tells what already happened.

Tillie (eats) lunch at school.

Mr. Keene ~~walked~~ in the halls.

Beans <u>will</u> wait for Tillie at home.

Writing

DIRECTIONS Look back at your opinion of Mr. Keene on page 78. Why do you think or feel that way? Write your reason using an example from the story.

I think Mr. Keene **Possible responses: is proud, happy, worried**

because **Possible responses: the students are learning, he loves his school, the kids work too hard.**

Children practice various conventions of standard English. Children write routinely for a range of tasks, purposes, and audiences.

Name _____

DIRECTIONS Say the word for each picture.
Write **ck** on the line if the word has the
same ending sound as .

1. ro **ck**

2. ba **ck**

3. fa _____

4. sa **ck**

5. pe _____

6. ja **ck**

7. pa **ck**

8. ca _____

Write two words that have the same ending sound as .

_____
Answers will vary but could include rock,
back, sack, and jack.

_____
Answers will vary but could include rock,
back, sack, and jack.

Children apply grade-level phonics and word
analysis skills.

Name _____

DIRECTIONS Choose a word from below and draw it in the box. Then write a sentence using the word.

announced   everything

Responses will vary.

Write in Response to Reading

DIRECTIONS Complete the sentence to tell what Tillie does at school.

Tillie Possible responses: builds dinosaurs, eats lunch, makes art, listens to Mr. Keene at school.

Children demonstrate contextual understanding of Benchmark Vocabulary. Children read text closely and use text evidence in their written answers.

Name _____

At the Rodeo

Have you ever seen a bucking bronco? How about a cowboy (roping) a calf? Come to the rodeo!

Rodeo cowboys and cowgirls show their skills. Cowboys on a ranch have these skills. First is the Grand Entry. The cowboys and cowgirls (gallop) into the arena on their horses. They (carry) American flags. It is exciting!

Next, the cowboys (rope) calves. A cowboy on a horse (twirls) his lariat. A lariat is a long rope with a loop on the end. He must quickly (catch) a calf with the rope. Real cowboys do this job on a ranch.

Then rodeo clowns come out. They wear Western clothes and clown makeup. They're funny! Next is bronc riding. The bronc is chosen because it acts like a wild horse. The cowboy (holds on) to the horse with one strap. He tries to stay on. The cowboy who (stays on) longest wins.

Rodeos started long ago. Cowboys were the biggest stars in the West. Rodeos are still fun!

Children read text closely to determine what the text says.

Name _____

Look for Clues

On page 83, circle the action words that show what cowboys and cowgirls are able to do.

Ask Questions

On page 83, find the rodeo event that you have questions about. Underline it.

Responses will vary, but children should choose Grand Entry, calf roping, rodeo clown act, or bronc riding.

Make Your Case

Circle the word in this sentence that tells how the writer feels about the rodeo: The rodeo is scary/fun.

Make Your Case: Extend Your Ideas

Write how you feel about the rodeo. Finish the sentence:

_____

The rodeo is _____ .

Does your answer show you agree with the writer? Why or why not?

Responses will vary, but children should write "feeling" words that indicate an opinion. Children should also correctly state if they agree or disagree with the writer's opinion and explain why.

Children read text closely to determine what the text says.

Name _____

DIRECTIONS Circle the words that need capital letters. Then write the sentence.

(jane) will have a party on (july) 4.

Jane will have a party on July 4.

DIRECTIONS Write an opinion about a character in *A Fine, Fine School.*

I think character _____

is characteristic _____ because

reasoning _____

_____ .

Children practice various conventions of standard English. Children write routinely for a range of tasks, purposes, and audiences.

Name _____

DIRECTIONS Choose a word from below and draw it in the box. Then write a sentence using the word.

office   worried

Responses will vary.

DIRECTIONS Choose one character from *A Fine, Fine School.* Write about the character on the lines below.

Possible response: Mr. Keene is proud of his school.

Children demonstrate contextual understanding of Benchmark Vocabulary. Children read text closely and use text evidence in their written answers.

Name _____

DIRECTIONS Add " " to each sentence.

"Come here," Tillie said.

"We don't want school in the summer," the teachers said.

Writing

DIRECTIONS Pretend you are a character from *A Fine, Fine School*. You talk to Mr. Keene about his decision to have more school. Complete the sentence below.

Mr. Keene, I think _Possible response: we shouldn't have to come to school on the weekends and holidays. We don't get to see our families._

Children practice various conventions of standard English. Children write routinely for a range of tasks, purposes, and audiences.

Benchmark Vocabulary

DIRECTIONS Choose a word from below and draw it in the box. Then write a sentence using the word.

enormous   cheer

Responses will vary.

Write in Response to Reading

DIRECTIONS Complete the sentence.

Mr. Keene says there will be no school on the weekends, holidays, or summer. I think this makes Tillie feel

Possible response: happy because

Possible response: she wants to play with her brother and her dog, Beans

Children demonstrate contextual understanding of Benchmark Vocabulary. Children read text closely and use text evidence in their written answers.

Name _____

DIRECTIONS Circle the words that describe the nouns.
Then write your own sentence with adjectives.

We go to a (fine) school on a (busy) street.

Responses will vary but should include adjectives.

DIRECTIONS Write a reason to support your opinion.

Responses will vary.

Children practice various conventions of
standard English. Children write routinely for a
range of tasks, purposes, and audiences.

Name _____

DIRECTIONS Say the word for each picture.
Write **i** on the line if you hear the **short i** sound.

 p<u>i</u>g

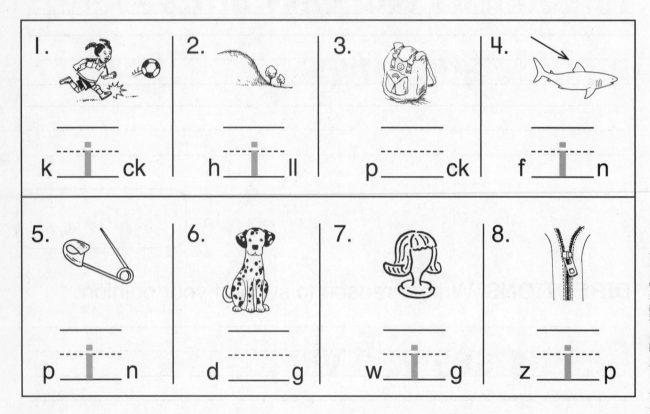

1. k___i___ck

2. h___i___ll

3. p_____ck

4. f___i___n

5. p___i___n

6. d_____g

7. w___i___g

8. z___i___p

Circle the word to finish each sentence. Write it on the line.

9. I __will__ go.

     (will)   wall

10. Sam __hid__ the mat.

     hip   (hid)

Children apply grade-level phonics and word
analysis skills.

Name _____

DIRECTIONS Draw the word below in the box. Then write a sentence using the word.

younger

[box]

Responses will vary.

Write in Response to Reading

DIRECTIONS Complete the sentence.

The school was fine again because Mr. Keene learned

Possible responses: school

cannot teach everything; learning

happens everywhere.

 Children demonstrate contextual understanding of Benchmark Vocabulary. Children read text closely and use text evidence in their written answers.

DIRECTIONS Add commas to each sentence.

We use crayons, pens, and paper at school.

Jane wants to learn about bugs, dogs, and flowers.

Writing

DIRECTIONS Write your group's opinion about *A Fine, Fine School.*

Responses will vary.

Children practice various conventions of standard English. Children write routinely for a range of tasks, purposes, and audiences.

Name _____

DIRECTIONS Draw the word below in the box. Then write a sentence using the word.

bullied

_____

Responses will vary.

Write in Response to Reading

DIRECTIONS Complete the sentence.

Mean Jean is **Possible responses:**

mean, bossy, selfish, pushy,

scary, loud, a bully.

Children demonstrate contextual understanding of Benchmark Vocabulary. Children read text closely and use text evidence in their written answers.

Name _____

DIRECTIONS Circle the words or phrases from *The Recess Queen* that appeal to your sense of hearing.

But when the recess bell went (ringity-ring,)

this kid ran (zingity-zing)

for the playground gate.

The kid you might scare with a jump

and a ("BOO") was too new

to know about Mean Jean the Recess Queen.

Find other words in the story that appeal to your senses. Write them on the lines below.

_____

Responses will vary but could

include snarled, thundered,

whizzed.

Children analyze and respond to literary and informational text.

Name _____

DIRECTIONS Circle the word that shows the action. Then circle when the action happens.

Sue (jumped) rope with me.   (past)   present   future

Sue (will play) with me later.   past   present   (future)

Writing

DIRECTIONS Write an opinion about one of the characters in *The Recess Queen.*

I think character _____

is description of character _____

_____

_____

_____

_____

Children practice various conventions of standard English. Children write routinely for a range of tasks, purposes, and audiences.

Phonics

Name _____

DIRECTIONS Say the word for each picture.
Write **x** on the line if the word has the same
ending sound as **ax**.

a<u>x</u>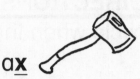

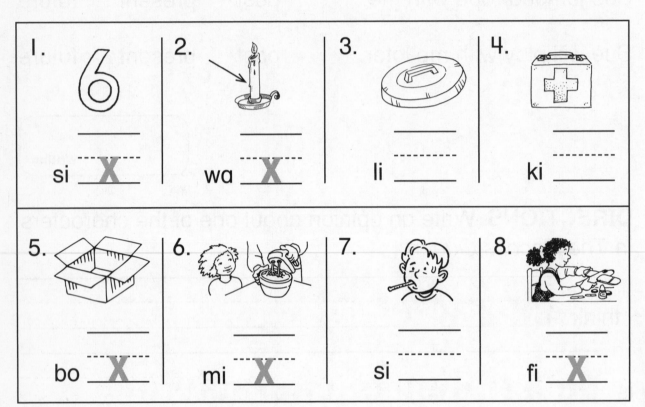

1. si __X__

2. wa __X__

3. li _____

4. ki _____

5. bo __X__

6. mi __X__

7. si _____

8. fi __X__

Write two words that have the same ending sound as 6.
Possible responses:
_____ fox _____   _____ mix _____

Read the sentence below. Underline the words that have the
same ending sound as **ax**.

He saw <u>six</u> <u>wax</u> cats.

 Children apply grade-level phonics and word
analysis skills.

Name _____

DIRECTIONS Draw the word below in the box. Then write a sentence using the word.

nobody

Responses will vary.

DIRECTIONS On the school playground, the children jumped. Write a sentence that uses the word *jumped.*

Possible response: The kids

jumped rope.

 Children demonstrate contextual understanding of Benchmark Vocabulary. Children read text closely and use text evidence in their written answers.

Name _____

DIRECTIONS Circle the word that can replace the underlined words in the sentence.

I will not tell <u>Sue or Jean.</u>   anywhere   (anyone)

Jean can go <u>on the swings or the slide.</u>   (anywhere)   anyone

Writing

DIRECTIONS Rewrite the opinion statement from Lesson 7 on page 95 to include a reason for your opinion.

Responses will vary.

Children practice various conventions of standard English. Children write routinely for a range of tasks, purposes, and audiences.

Name _____

DIRECTIONS Draw the word below in the box. Then write a sentence using the word.

tiny

```
┌──────────────────────────────────────────────┐
│                                                │
│                                                │
│                                                │
│                                                │
│                                                │
└──────────────────────────────────────────────┘
```

_____

Responses will vary.

Write in Response to Reading

DIRECTIONS Complete the sentence.

Mean Jean has a **Possible responses: noisy**
_____

voice, a **blaring, ear-piercing, roaring** voice,
_____

an **ear-splitting, screeching** voice.
_____

🏠 Children demonstrate contextual understanding of
Benchmark Vocabulary. Children read text closely
and use text evidence in their written answers.

Name _____

DIRECTIONS Circle the word that means the book belongs to Sue. Then write a sentence that uses that word.

Sue lost (her) book.

Responses will vary but should use the word *her.*

DIRECTIONS Write a new opinion about a character or an event. Circle the adjectives you use.

Responses will vary.

Children practice various conventions of standard English. Children write routinely for a range of tasks, purposes, and audiences.

Name _____

Benchmark Vocabulary

DIRECTIONS Choose a word from below and draw it in the box. Then write a sentence using the word.

snarled   bossy

```



```

_____

Responses will vary.

_____

Write in Response to Reading

DIRECTIONS Draw a picture of Jean or Katie Sue. Write words that tell about the character.

I drew **Jean or Katie Sue.**

She is **Possible responses: mean, bossy, pushy; puny, loony, quick, sassy.**

Children demonstrate contextual understanding of Benchmark Vocabulary. Children read text closely and use text evidence in their written answers.

Name _____

DIRECTIONS Circle the name of the person who says or does each thing.

Story Elements: Characters

1. Who growls, howls, snarls, and grabs?

   (Jean)   Katie Sue

2. Who is puny and loony?

   Jean   (Katie Sue)

3. Who says "How DID you get so bossy?"

   Jean   (Katie Sue)

4. Who says "Nobody kicks until Queen Jean kicks?"

   (Jean)   Katie Sue

Children analyze and respond to literary and informational text.

Name _____

DIRECTIONS Circle the word that describes the noun.

Mean Jean was a (bossy) girl.

She bullied (tiny) kids.

DIRECTIONS Write an opinion statement about your poster.

I think my poster is Possible responses: good, nice because Possible responses: it tells people to be nice.

Children practice various conventions of standard English. Children write routinely for a range of tasks, purposes, and audiences.

Name _____

DIRECTIONS Say the word for each picture.
Write **o** on the line if you hear the **short o** sound.

t_o_p

1. p **o** t

2. f **o** x

3. l **o** ck

4. b ___ t

5. w ___ b

6. r **o** ck

7. **o** x

8. d ___ ck

Write a word for each picture.

9.

sock

10.

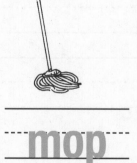

mop

Children apply grade-level phonics and word analysis skills.

Name _____

DIRECTIONS Choose a word from below and draw it in the box. Then write a sentence using the word.

dared   stared

Responses will vary.

Write in Response to Reading

DIRECTIONS Complete the sentence with a word that rhymes.

I like ice cream, I like tea, I want you to fly like a

_____

Possible responses: bee, flea.

Children demonstrate contextual understanding of Benchmark Vocabulary. Children read text closely and use text evidence in their written answers.

Name _____

DIRECTIONS Read these sentences from *The Recess Queen.* Circle two words that rhyme.

Then from the side a kid called out,

"Go, Jean, go!"

And too surprised to even shout,

Jean jumped in with Katie Sue.

Read the sentences again. Which two lines have the same rhythm? Underline them.

Find two other words that rhyme in the story.
Write them below.

_____

Responses will vary
but should be rhyming words.

_____

_____

_____

Children analyze and respond to literary and informational text.

Name _____

DIRECTIONS Complete the sentences using the word *I* or *me*.

_____

The kids in my class like __**me**__.

_____

__**I**__ want to play with my friends.

_____

Will you play with __**me**__?

DIRECTIONS Write the topic of your opinion piece.

Responses will vary.

_____

_____

_____

_____

_____

_____

_____

_____

Children practice various conventions of standard English. Children write routinely for a range of tasks, purposes, and audiences.

Name _____

DIRECTIONS Choose a word from below and draw it in the box. Then write a sentence using the word.

giggled   disaster

Responses will vary.

Write in Response to Reading

DIRECTIONS Complete the sentence to tell what Jean learns.

A friend should Possible response: share.

A friend should not Possible response: be mean.

Children demonstrate contextual understanding of Benchmark Vocabulary. Children read text closely and use text evidence in their written answers.

Name _____

DIRECTIONS Use a word in the box to complete the sentences below.

everyone	everything

I like _____everything_____ about school.

Jean is mean to _____everyone_____ at school.

DIRECTIONS Write your opinion about one of the texts. Write a reason that supports your opinion.

Responses will vary.

_____

_____

_____

_____

_____

_____

_____

Children practice various conventions of standard English. Children write routinely for a range of tasks, purposes, and audiences.

DIRECTIONS Circle a word to match each picture.

 pan**s**

1. bat (bats)	2. (mop) mops
3. rock (rocks)	4. pig (pigs)
5. top (tops)	6. cap (caps)
7. (kit) kits	8. sack (sacks)

Write a sentence for each word.

9. cats Possible response: Cats can sleep anywhere.

10. fans Possible response: We have fans in our house.

Children apply grade-level phonics and word analysis skills.

Name _____

DIRECTIONS Choose a word from below and draw it in the box. Then write a sentence using the word.

learning   everything

Responses will vary.

Copyright © Pearson Education, Inc., or its affiliates. All Rights Reserved.

Write in Response to Reading

The endings of *A Fine, Fine School* and *The Recess Queen* are alike in some ways. At the ending of both stories, the characters feel

Possible response: happy.

Children demonstrate contextual understanding of Benchmark Vocabulary. Children read text closely and use text evidence in their written answers.

Name _____

Children's Day

Today is May 5. It is Children's Day! This is the best holiday.

I put on a kimono. It is like a robe. My sisters and I are lucky. My father works at a kimono factory. We have a lot of kimonos!

The smell of iris flowers fills the air. Today my brother uses the leaves of this plant as a sword. He is dressed like a Japanese warrior called a samurai.

I am excited to help hang paper carp outside. A carp is a kind of fish. Carp are strong. Our parents want us to be strong like carp.

I cannot wait to see my cousins. We go to their house and play games. Then we eat mochi (MOH-chee) rice. It is sweet.

My parents make Children's Day special. They want us to be strong. They have hopes for us. Children's Day is fun and makes me feel proud.

Children read text closely to determine what the text says.

Name _____

Look for Clues

Circle the sentence that tells what the parents do for Children's Day.

Children should circle "My parents make Children's Day special."

What do the parents want their children to be like?

strong like carp

Ask Questions

On page 112, find the part that you would like to know more about. Draw a box around it.   **Responses will vary.**

Make Your Case

On page 112, underline sentences that tell why the girl likes Children's Day.

Children should underline "I am excited to help hang paper carp outside" and "I cannot wait to see my cousins."

Would you like to have Children's Day here? Tell a partner what you think and why.

Responses will vary, but children should give a reason for their responses.

Children read text closely to determine what the text says.

Name _____

DIRECTIONS Use **but**, **or**, or **so** to complete the sentences below.

Mean Jean was a bully, ____**but**____ now she is nice.

She is nice, ____**so**____ kids like her.

DIRECTIONS Write your opinion with at least one detail added to it.

Responses will vary.

Children practice various conventions of standard English. Children write routinely for a range of tasks, purposes, and audiences.

Name _____

DIRECTIONS Add **-s** to each word.
Write the new word on the line.

1. hop _____ **hops** _____ | 2. pat _____ **pats** _____

3. hug _____ **hugs** _____ | 4. dig _____ **digs** _____

Use the words you wrote to finish the sentences.
Write the words on the lines.

5. The dog _____ **digs** _____ it up.

6. The dog _____ **hops** _____ on Jill.

7. Sam _____ **pats** _____ the dog.

8. Pam _____ **hugs** _____ the dog.

Children apply grade-level phonics and word
analysis skills.

Name _____

DIRECTIONS Choose a word from below and draw it in the box. Then write a sentence using the word.

perfect   tidy

Responses will vary.

Write in Response to Reading

DIRECTIONS Write your answer on the lines below.

Why does Bryan's family move to China?

Responses will vary but should include that his mom gets a new job there.

Children demonstrate contextual understanding of Benchmark Vocabulary. Children read text closely and use text evidence in their written answers.

Name _____

DIRECTIONS Think about what happens at the beginning, in the middle, and at the end of *Far from Home.* Then answer the questions below.

What is one thing that happens at the beginning of the story?

Responses will vary but should include something that happens before the family is in China.

What is one thing that happens in the middle of the story?

Responses will vary but should include something that happens at school in China.

What is one thing that happens at the end of the story?

Responses will vary but should include something that happens during or after the painting lesson.

Children analyze and respond to literary texts.

Unit 2 • Module B • Lesson 1 • 117

DIRECTIONS Circle the action words that tell what Bryan does.

Bryan (moves) to China.

Bryan (uses) chopsticks.

Bryan (learns) kung fu.

Writing

DIRECTIONS Look at the illustration you drew. Write a sentence that tells a fact about your illustration.

Responses will vary.

Children practice various conventions of standard English. Children write routinely for a range of tasks, purposes, and audiences.

Name _____

DIRECTIONS Choose a word from below and draw it in the box. Then write a sentence using the word.

tucked   strange

_____

Responses will vary.

Write in Response to Reading

DIRECTIONS Complete the sentence.

One thing Bryan learns at school is Responses

will vary but should include a

skill or lesson he learned at

school in China.

Children demonstrate contextual understanding of Benchmark Vocabulary. Children read text closely and use text evidence in their written answers.

Name _____

DIRECTIONS Think about what the illustrations on pages 10 and 11 show. Then answer the questions below.

What is one thing you learn about a character from the illustrations?

Responses will vary but should include a detail about Bryan or Tao.

What is one thing you learn about a setting from the illustrations? Responses will vary but should include a detail about the lunchroom or the place where children have recess.

What is one thing you learn about an event from the illustrations? Responses will vary but should include details about what happens during recess or lunchtime.

Children analyze and respond to literary texts.

Name _____

DIRECTIONS Write each sentence again using a pronoun.

Mom gets a job.

_____

She gets a job. _____

Bryan likes basketball.

_____

He likes basketball. _____

Writing

DIRECTIONS Complete the sentence.

This book is about Responses will vary

but should include going to a

new school in a new country.

.

Children practice various conventions of standard English. Children write routinely for a range of tasks, purposes, and audiences.

Name _____

DIRECTIONS Add **-ing** to each word. Write it on the line.

1. sell _____selling_____

2. look _____looking_____

3. fix _____fixing_____

4. lick _____licking_____

Use the words you wrote to finish the sentences.
Write the words on the lines.

5. The man is _____fixing_____ it.

6. Sam is _____looking_____ at the bug.

7. The big cat is _____licking_____ the little cat.

8. Jen is _____selling_____ cups.

Children apply grade-level phonics and word analysis skills.

Name _____

DIRECTIONS Choose a word from below and draw it in the box. Then write a sentence using the word.

neatly   shocked

```
┌──────────────────────────────────────────────┐
│                                                │
│                                                │
│                                                │
│                                                │
└──────────────────────────────────────────────┘
```

Responses will vary.

Write in Response to Reading

DIRECTIONS Complete the sentence.

One way Bryan likes to be perfect is _Responses will vary but could include that he never breaks rules, that he always does his homework, or that his shirt is tucked in._

 Children demonstrate contextual understanding of Benchmark Vocabulary. Children read text closely and use text evidence in their written answers.

Name _____

DIRECTIONS Write the sentence again using a pronoun.

Bryan and Tao paint with ink.

They paint with ink.

Writing

DIRECTIONS Draw a picture of something you learned about China. Then write a sentence about your drawing.

Responses will vary.

Children practice various conventions of standard English. Children write routinely for a range of tasks, purposes, and audiences.

Name _____

DIRECTIONS Choose a word from below and draw it in the box. Then write a sentence using the word.

promised   exercise

Responses will vary.

Write in Response to Reading

DIRECTIONS Write your answer on the lines below.

What is different about the school in China?

Responses will vary but could include that children exercise at recess or that they use chopsticks at lunch.

Children demonstrate contextual understanding of Benchmark Vocabulary. Children read text closely and use text evidence in their written answers.

Name _____

DIRECTIONS Circle the right word.

Bryan enjoys (his him he) new school.

Tao and Bryan like (they theirs their) painting.

Writing

DIRECTIONS Choose an event or illustration. Write a sentence that tells a fact about it.

_____

Responses will vary.

_____

_____

_____

_____

_____

_____

Children practice various conventions of standard English. Children write routinely for a range of tasks, purposes, and audiences.

Name _____

DIRECTIONS Choose a word from below and draw it in the box. Then write a sentence using the word.

enjoy   lesson

Responses will vary.

Write in Response to Reading

DIRECTIONS Complete the sentence.

Bryan enjoys Responses will vary but could include learning kung fu or his first day of school.

Children demonstrate contextual understanding of Benchmark Vocabulary. Children read text closely and use text evidence in their written answers.

Name _____

DIRECTIONS Circle the words that tell about a noun.

Bryan lives in a (tidy) house.

The (nice) boy says hello.

Bryan spills (black) ink.

DIRECTIONS Choose an illustration. Think about what it shows. Then write a caption for the illustration.

Responses will vary.

Children practice various conventions of standard English. Children write routinely for a range of tasks, purposes, and audiences.

Name _____

DIRECTIONS Circle the word for each picture.

1. mitt (men) man

2. (bed) bid bad

3. pan pin (pen)

4. tin tan (ten)

5. (jet) jam jog

6. not (net) nip

Circle the word that completes each sentence.
Write it on the line.

7. The fat _____ **hen** _____ sits on my lap.

   (hen)   hat

8. I like my big _____ **red** _____ hat.

   rid   (red)

Children apply grade-level phonics and word analysis skills.

Name _____

DIRECTIONS Choose a word from below and draw it in the box. Then write a sentence using the word.

countries   villages   learn

Responses will vary.

Write in Response to Reading

DIRECTIONS Write your answer on the lines below.

What is this book all about?

Responses will vary but should include that it is about schools around the world.

Children demonstrate contextual understanding of Benchmark Vocabulary. Children read text closely and use text evidence in their written answers.

Name _____

DIRECTIONS Add the correct word to each sentence.

at   during

_____

We go to school _____ **during** _____ the day.

_____

I sit _____ **at** _____ my desk.

Writing

DIRECTIONS Look at your illustration. Write a sentence that tells about it.

Responses will vary.

Children practice various conventions of standard English. Children write routinely for a range of tasks, purposes, and audiences.

Name _____

DIRECTIONS Choose a word from below and draw it in the box. Then write a sentence using the word.

languages   community   weather

Responses will vary.

Write in Response to Reading

What is one thing Maria studies in school?

Responses will vary but could include Dari or math.

What is one thing Rosita studies in school?

Responses will vary but could include reading, drawing, or math.

Children demonstrate contextual understanding of Benchmark Vocabulary. Children read text closely and use text evidence in their written answers.

Name _____

DIRECTIONS Add these missing words to the sentence.

with	to

Children go ____**to**____ school ____**with**____ friends.

DIRECTIONS Choose one child to write about. Complete the graphic organizer.

Responses will vary.

Web B

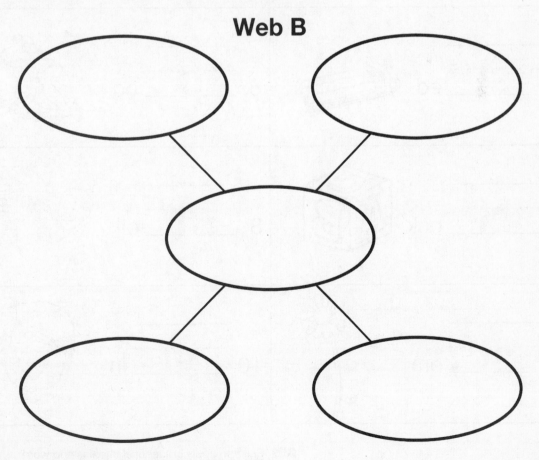

Children practice various conventions of standard English. Children write routinely for a range of tasks, purposes, and audiences.

Name _____

DIRECTIONS Pick letters from the box to finish each word. Write the letters on the line.

bl	cl	cr	dr	fl	fr	gr	sl	sm	st

1. _____ **fl** _____ ag

2. _____ **cr** _____ ab

3. _____ **cl** _____ ap

4. _____ **dr** _____ ess

5. _____ **sl** _____ ed
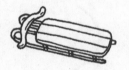

6. _____ **fr** _____ og

7. _____ **bl** _____ ock

8. _____ **sm** _____ ell

9. _____ **st** _____ em

10. _____ **gr** _____ in

Children apply grade-level phonics and word analysis skills.

Name _____

DIRECTIONS Choose a word from below and draw it in the box. Then write a sentence using the word.

native   library   subject

Responses will vary.

Write in Response to Reading

DIRECTIONS Complete the sentences below.

Levi likes to Responses will vary but could include work with computers.

Daisuke likes Responses will vary but could include science or dinosaurs.

Children demonstrate contextual understanding of Benchmark Vocabulary. Children read text closely and use text evidence in their written answers.

Name _____

Pizza, Pizza Everywhere

Do you like to eat pizza? I sure do! Pizza is the most interesting food ever!

In America many people like cheese on pizza. I like to eat pepperoni on pizza too. I have eaten pizza all around the world. Not everyone likes the same toppings. I thought some toppings were strange. I found out that they were yummy!

In India, I tried sheep and tofu on pizza. In France, I ate bacon on pizza. In Australia, I tried shrimp and pineapple. In Costa Rica, I had coconut pizza. Are you looking for a new way to eat peas? Then go to Brazil. Many people like peas on their pizza there. I can't wait to try more toppings on pizza!

Think about the toppings the next time you want pizza. Try something new. Enjoy!

Children read text closely to determine what the text says.

Name _____

Look for Clues

On page 136, circle the sentence that tells you the writer thinks pizza is interesting.

Circled: Pizza is the most interesting food ever!

Ask Questions

Write two questions you might ask the author about pizza.

Responses will vary but could include: Which topping did you like best? Which topping did you like least?

Make Your Case

On page 136, draw a box around something you learned from the text that you think is interesting. Responses will vary.

Prove It!

If you could try one of the pizza toppings described in the text, which would you try? Tell a partner which topping you picked and why.

Responses will vary, but children should name one of the toppings described in the text and give a reason for their choice.

 Children read text closely to determine what the text says.

Name _____

DIRECTIONS Fill in the correct verb in the sentence.

play   plays

_____

Friends ___ **play** ___ games together.

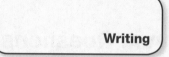

Writing

DIRECTIONS Choose one child to write about. Complete the graphic organizer.

Responses will vary.

Web B

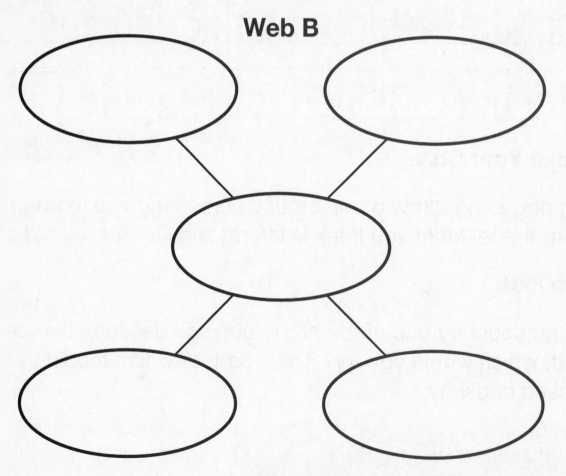

Children practice various conventions of standard English. Children write routinely for a range of tasks, purposes, and audiences.

Name _____

DIRECTIONS Choose a word from below and draw it in the box. Then write a sentence using the word.

ballet   classmates

Responses will vary.

Write in Response to Reading

DIRECTIONS Complete the sentences.

Olia wants to Responses will vary but should include being a ballet dancer.

At recess Sbongile likes to Responses will vary but should include playing ball games or swimming.

Children demonstrate contextual understanding of Benchmark Vocabulary. Children read text closely and use text evidence in their written answers.

Name _____

DIRECTIONS Circle the words that need capital letters.

Maria lives in (kabul,) a city in (afghanistan.)

Levi goes to school on the coast of (baffin) (island.)

Writing

DIRECTIONS Think about the two children you chose.
Write a sentence that tells how they are alike.

Responses will vary.

Children practice various conventions of standard
English. Children write routinely for a range of tasks,
purposes, and audiences.

Name _____

DIRECTIONS Choose a word from below and draw it in the box. Then write a sentence using the word.

blind   diagrams   city

Responses will vary.

Write in Response to Reading

DIRECTIONS Write your answer on the lines below.

What is one way Samantha and Chavy are alike?

Responses will vary but could include that both go to school, play sports, or study math.

Children demonstrate contextual understanding of Benchmark Vocabulary. Children read text closely and use text evidence in their written answers.

Name _____

DIRECTIONS Circle the words that need capital letters.

(olia) and (sbongile) study English.

At recess (aseye) plays clapping games.

Writing

DIRECTIONS Think about the two children you chose.
Write a sentence that tells how they are different.

Responses will vary.

Children practice various conventions of standard
English. Children write routinely for a range of tasks,
purposes, and audiences.

Name _____

DIRECTIONS Say the word for each picture. Write **u** on the line if you hear the **short u** sound.

p**u**p

1. _____ b ___**u**___ g	2. _____ d ___**u**___ ck
3. _____ b ___**u**___ s	4. _____ h ___**u**___ g
5. _____ b _____ x	6. _____ dr ___**u**___ m
7. _____ s ___**u**___ n	8. _____ sw _____ m

Children apply grade-level phonics and word analysis skills.

Name _____

DIRECTIONS Choose a word from below and draw it in the box. Then write a sentence using the word.

enjoy   subject

Responses will vary.

Write in Response to Reading

DIRECTIONS Write your answer on the lines.

How is your school like a school we read about?

Responses will vary.

Children demonstrate contextual understanding of Benchmark Vocabulary. Children read text closely and use text evidence in their written answers.

Name _____

DIRECTIONS Draw a picture that shows the main topic of *Going to School.* Then write a sentence that tells the main topic.

Responses will vary but should include that children around the world go to school.

Children analyze and respond to informational texts.

Name _____

DIRECTIONS Write the sentences again. Add capital letters and end marks where needed.

The dance school is in moscow

_____

The dance school is in Moscow.

Moscow is a city in russia

_____

Moscow is a city in Russia.

Writing

DIRECTIONS Think about details you can add to your writing. Write your revised sentences.

_____

Responses will vary.

_____

_____

_____

_____

_____

Children practice various conventions of standard English. Children write routinely for a range of tasks, purposes, and audiences.

Name _____

DIRECTIONS Choose a word from below and draw it in the box. Then write a sentence using the word.

lesson   classmates

Responses will vary.

Write in Response to Reading

DIRECTIONS Complete the sentence.

I would like to go to school in _____

because Responses will vary.

Children demonstrate contextual understanding of Benchmark Vocabulary. Children read text closely and use text evidence in their written answers.

Name _____

DIRECTIONS Write a sentence that tells how *Far from Home* and *Going to School* are different. Use examples from the texts.

_____

Responses will vary but should include that *Far from Home* is about a boy who goes to a

new school in China. It is a made-up story. *Going to School* is about children at different

schools around the world. It is true.

Children analyze and respond to literary and informational texts.

Name _____

DIRECTIONS Add the correct word to the sentences.

a   an

_____

Aseye wants to be _____ a _____ doctor.

_____

Bryan takes _____ an _____ art class.

Writing

DIRECTIONS Copy your sentences on the lines. Use your best handwriting.

_____

Responses will vary.

_____

_____

_____

Children practice various conventions of standard English. Children write routinely for a range of tasks, purposes, and audiences.

Name _____

DIRECTIONS Say the word for each picture. Circle the letters that finish each word. Write the letters on the line.

(nd) nt 1. po __nd__	nt (mp) 2. ju __mp__
mp (nt) 3. pla __nt__	(st) nt 4. ca __st__
st (mp) 5. la __mp__	nt (nd) 6. ha __nd__
(st) nt 7. ve __st__	(nt) mp 8. te __nt__
nt (st) 9. ne __st__	(mp) st 10. sta __mp__

Children apply grade-level phonics and word analysis skills.

Name _____

DIRECTIONS Say the word for each picture.
Write **sh** or **th** to finish the word.

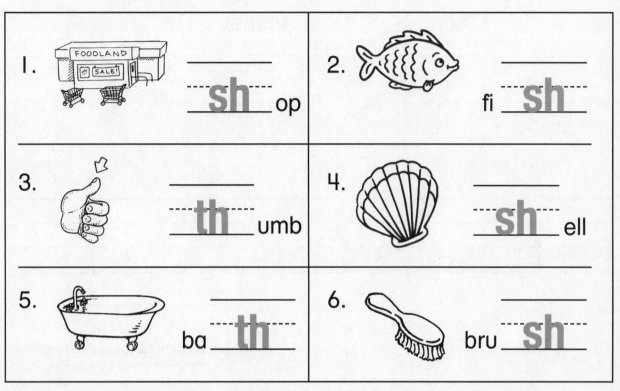

1. ___**sh**___ op

2. fi ___**sh**___

3. ___**th**___ umb

4. ___**sh**___ ell

5. ba ___**th**___

6. bru ___**sh**___

Circle a word to finish each sentence. Write the word.

path   math

7. She walked on the bike ___**path**___ .

drip   ship

8. I saw the ___**ship**___ .

Children apply grade-level phonics and
word analysis skills.

Name _____

DIRECTIONS Choose a word from below and draw it in the box. Then write a sentence using the word.

trophy   money

_____

Responses will vary. _____

Write in Response to Reading

DIRECTIONS Write your answer on the lines below. How does the team use the prize money?

_____

Responses will vary but should _____

include that they fix another _____

team's soccer field. _____

Children demonstrate contextual understanding of Benchmark Vocabulary. Children read text closely and use text evidence in their written answers.

Name _____

DIRECTIONS Write the correct pronoun on the line.

He	They

_____

Carlos had an idea. _____He_____ had an idea.

DIRECTIONS Take notes about the story events on the lines below.

_____

Beginning <u>Responses will vary but should include that Las Águilas School won the</u>

_____

<u>soccer tournament. The soccer team got to decide how to spend the prize money.</u>

_____

Middle <u>Responses will vary but should include something about the earthquake.</u>

_____

_____

End <u>Responses will vary but should include Las Águilas School giving the money to</u>

_____

<u>Los Leones School to fix their soccer field.</u>

Children practice various conventions of standard English. Children write routinely for a range of tasks, purposes, and audiences.

Name _____

DIRECTIONS Choose a word from below and draw it in the box. Then write a sentence using the word.

golden   spend   gasped

Responses will vary.

Write in Response to Reading

DIRECTIONS Write your answer on the lines below.
What does the team get for winning the soccer tournament?

Responses will vary but could include that the team gets a trophy and some prize money.

Children demonstrate contextual understanding of Benchmark Vocabulary. Children read text closely and use text evidence in their written answers.

Name _____

DIRECTIONS Write the correct pronoun on the line.

their	her

_____

Patricia walks home with ___**her**___ mom.

DIRECTIONS Write a sentence about the beginning of the story. Then write a sentence about the middle of the story.

Sentence 1: Possible response: Las Águilas School won the soccer tournament.

The soccer team gets to decide how to spend the prize money.

Sentence 2: Possible response: The soccer team survived an earthquake on the

soccer field.

Children practice various conventions of standard English. Children write routinely for a range of tasks, purposes, and audiences.

Name _____

DIRECTIONS Circle a word to finish each sentence.
Write it on the line.

 small smell

1. Look at the ___small___ cat go up!

tell tall

2. It is too ___tall___ for us.

call sell

3. We can ___call___ Dad.

wall walk

4. Dad will ___walk___ up.

talk tell

5. We have a ___talk___ with Dad.

Children apply grade-level phonics and word
analysis skills.

Name _____

DIRECTIONS Draw a picture of the word below in the box. Then write a sentence using the word.

teammates

Responses will vary.

Write in Response to Reading

DIRECTIONS Complete the sentence.

Juan's idea is Responses will vary but should include putting a chocolate fountain in the middle of the soccer field.

Children demonstrate contextual understanding of Benchmark Vocabulary. Children read text closely and use text evidence in their written answers.

Name _____

Are You My Kitten?

"Are you my kitten?" Kelly asked. The kitten was black with white paws. Kelly wasn't sure. She saw another kitten. It was gray with a white face. "Are you my kitten?" Kelly still wasn't sure.

Kelly looked at a third kitten. It was gray and black and white all over. It curled up beside its brother and sister in Mrs. Bell's yard. Mrs. Bell's cat had had three kittens.

The kitten touched Kelly's hand with a soft paw. "You are my kitten!" Kelly said. "I will take you home. I will feed you and give you water. I will give you a place to sleep. I will play with you. You are definitely my kitten!"

Children read text closely to determine what the text says.

Name _____

Look for Clues

Circle the words on page 158 that tell what the third kitten looks like.

Children should circle the words gray, black, and white.

Ask Questions

On page 158, underline a sentence about taking care of a kitten that you would like to know more about.

Responses will vary.

Make Your Case

Draw the kitten you would choose. Write words to describe it.

Responses will vary, but children should draw a kitten and write at least two descriptive words.

 Children read text closely to determine what the text says.

Name _____

DIRECTIONS Circle the words that tell about a noun.

Carlos wants to make a (large) pool.

The team likes the (old) uniforms.

A (round) fountain will get in the way.

DIRECTIONS Write a sentence about the end of the story.

Responses will vary but should include that the soccer team from Las Águilas School used the tournament money to fix the soccer field at Los Leones School.

Children practice various conventions of standard English. Children write routinely for a range of tasks, purposes, and audiences.

Name _____

DIRECTIONS Choose a word from below and draw it in the box. Then write a sentence using the word.

safe   brave

Responses will vary.

Write in Response to Reading

DIRECTIONS Write your answer on the lines below. What does Coach Ramos do after the earthquake?

Responses will vary but could include that he makes sure nobody is hurt and calls the principal.

 Children demonstrate contextual understanding of Benchmark Vocabulary. Children read text closely and use text evidence in their written answers.

Name _____

DIRECTIONS Circle the word that shows who owns the field.

The (team's / team) field was better than ever.

DIRECTIONS Add time or sequence words to your sentences. Write the sentences on the lines below.

Responses will vary but should include words such as first, next, then, and last.

Children practice various conventions of standard English. Children write routinely for a range of tasks, purposes, and audiences.

Name _____

DIRECTIONS Choose a word from below and draw it in the box. Then write a sentence using the word.

damage   zooming

[drawing box]

Responses will vary.

Write in Response to Reading

DIRECTIONS Complete the sentence.

One way the earthquake causes damage is

Responses will vary but could include that windows are broken or that there is a crack in the street or in the soccer field.

Children demonstrate contextual understanding of Benchmark Vocabulary. Children read text closely and use text evidence in their written answers.

DIRECTIONS Circle the word to use to put the two sentences together.

(and)   but   or

Patricia saw the ruined field. She had an idea.

Writing

DIRECTIONS Think about details you can add to your sentences. Rewrite the sentences below.

Responses will vary.

Children practice various conventions of standard English. Children write routinely for a range of tasks, purposes, and audiences.

Name _____

DIRECTIONS Circle the word for each picture.

1. (rake) rack	2. snack (snake)	3. frog (frame)
4. (can) cane	5. (cape) cap	6. (plane) plan

Choose a word to finish each sentence.
Write the word on the line.

lake   lock

7. I like to swim in the _____ **lake** _____.

plant   plate

8. Please put the food on the _____ **plate** _____.

gum   game

9. Will you play this _____ **game** _____ with me?

Children apply grade-level phonics and
word analysis skills.

Name _____

DIRECTIONS Choose a word from below and draw it in the box. Then write a sentence using the word.

need   want   position

┌───┐
│   │
│   │
│   │
│   │
│   │
└───┘

_____

Responses will vary.

_____

Write in Response to Reading

DIRECTIONS Complete the sentence.

The team wants to Responses will vary

but should include that they want

to fix another team's soccer field.

_____

Children demonstrate contextual understanding of Benchmark Vocabulary. Children read text closely and use text evidence in their written answers.

Name _____

DIRECTIONS Rewrite the two sentences as one sentence. Use one of the words in the box.

and	but	or

The field looked great. Patricia felt proud.

The field looked great, and

Patricia felt proud.

DIRECTIONS Look at your illustration. Write about what happens.

Responses will vary.

Children practice various conventions of standard English. Children write routinely for a range of tasks, purposes, and audiences.

Name _____

DIRECTIONS Choose a word from below and draw it in the box. Then write a sentence using the word.

coins   bills

Responses will vary.

Write in Response to Reading

DIRECTIONS Complete the sentence.

Hunter wants to buy _____ a skateboard _____

Children demonstrate contextual understanding of Benchmark Vocabulary. Children read text closely and use text evidence in their written answers.

Name _____

DIRECTIONS Draw a picture that shows the narrator of page 9 in the story. Then write a sentence that tells how you know this is the narrator.

Responses will vary but could include that the narrator's words are in a speech bubble or that she uses the words *us* and *I*.

 Children analyze and respond to literary texts.

Conventions

DIRECTIONS Rewrite the two sentences as one sentence. Use one of the words in the box.

and	but	or

Hunter wants a skateboard. He doesn't want that one.

Hunter wants a skateboard, but he doesn't want that one.

Writing

DIRECTIONS Write about the story events in order.

Possible response: First, the bills and coins are in the jar. Hunter is saving money to buy a

skateboard. Then, Hunter gets some money for his birthday. So he goes to the toy store.

But he only has enough money to buy a cheaper skateboard. Next, he sells his old toys and

does some chores. Finally he has enough money to buy the skateboard that he wanted.

Children practice various conventions of standard English. Children write routinely for a range of tasks, purposes, and audiences.

Name _____

DIRECTIONS Circle the word for each picture. Write it on the line.

 la<u>ce</u>

 a<u>ge</u>

1. (face) fake	2. rake (race)	3. (wag) wage
face	**race**	**wag**
4.  speck (space)	5. 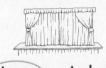 (stage) stake	6.  pace (page)
space	**stage**	**page**

Circle the word to finish each sentence. Write the word.

(lace)   brake

7. I tripped on my ____**lace**____ .

page   (cage)

8. My pet bird lives in a ____**cage**____ .

 Children apply grade-level phonics and word analysis skills.

Unit 3 • Module A • Lesson 8 • 171

Name _____

DIRECTIONS Choose a word from below and draw it in the box. Then write a sentence using the word.

shiny   bossy

Responses will vary.

Write in Response to Reading

DIRECTIONS Write your answer on the lines.

Who lives in Hunter's money jar?

Responses will vary but could include Scratch, Ridge, Hex, Rip, and other coins and bills.

Children demonstrate contextual understanding of Benchmark Vocabulary. Children read text closely and use text evidence in their written answers.

Name _____

DIRECTIONS Find the word with an ending.
Underline the root word. Circle the ending.

The boy counted his money every day.

Writing

DIRECTIONS Think about a time when you made a choice. Write your idea on the lines.

Responses will vary.

_____

_____

_____

_____

_____

_____

_____

_____

_____

_____

_____

Children practice various conventions of standard English. Children write routinely for a range of tasks, purposes, and audiences.

Name _____

DIRECTIONS Choose a word from below and draw it in the box. Then write a sentence using the word.

count   bank

Responses will vary.

Write in Response to Reading

DIRECTIONS Write your answer on the lines below.

What does Hunter do with his money?

Responses will vary but should include that he takes his money to the toy store.

Children demonstrate contextual understanding of Benchmark Vocabulary. Children read text closely and use text evidence in their written answers.

Name _____

DIRECTIONS Circle the correct pronoun.

Hunter does not count (our / his) money.

DIRECTIONS Review your events. Then write about the events below.

Responses will vary.

Children practice various conventions of standard English. Children write routinely for a range of tasks, purposes, and audiences.

Name _____

DIRECTIONS Choose a word from below and draw it in the box. Then write a sentence using the word.

sell   waste   earn

Responses will vary.

DIRECTIONS Write your answer on the lines below.

Why does Scratch think Hunter should keep saving his money?

Responses will vary but should include that she doesn't want Hunter to waste his money on a skateboard that isn't as good.

Children demonstrate contextual understanding of Benchmark Vocabulary. Children read text closely and use text evidence in their written answers.

DIRECTIONS Write two words from your web. Then write the meanings of the words below.

_____

Word 1: Responses will vary but should include one of these words and its meaning:

_____

_____

buy, sell, earn, waste, saving, cheaper, coins, bills.

_____

_____

Word 2: Responses will vary but should include one of these words and its meaning:

_____

_____

buy, sell, earn, waste, saving, cheaper, coins, bills.

_____

_____

Children analyze and respond to literary texts.

Lesson 10

Name _____

Conventions

DIRECTIONS Add commas to the sentence.

Scratch, Hex, and Ridge all live in the money jar.

Writing

DIRECTIONS Think about how your story ends. Write the ending events below.

Responses will vary.

Children practice various conventions of standard English. Children write routinely for a range of tasks, purposes, and audiences.

Name _____

DIRECTIONS Circle the word for each picture.

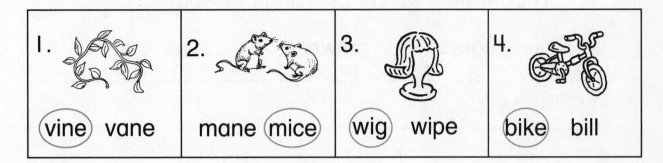

1. (vine) vane

2. mane (mice)

3. (wig) wipe

4. (bike) bill

Say the name of each picture.
Write the word on the line.

5. slide

6. five

7. kite

Pick a word to finish each sentence.
Write the word on the line.

slice   price

8. I will eat a _____ slice _____ .

bite   rice

9. Do you want a _____ bite _____ ?

Children apply grade-level phonics and
word analysis skills.

Name _____

DIRECTIONS Choose a word from below and draw it in the box. Then write a sentence using the word.

chores   crowded   piles

Responses will vary.

Write in Response to Reading

DIRECTIONS Write your answer on the lines.

What happens at the end of the story?

Responses will vary but should include that Hunter buys a skateboard.

Children demonstrate contextual understanding of Benchmark Vocabulary. Children read text closely and use text evidence in their written answers.

Name _____

DIRECTIONS Circle the correct verb.

Hunter (looked / looks / will look) at the skateboard last week.

Writing

DIRECTIONS Write your revised story on the lines.

Responses will vary.

Children practice various conventions of standard English. Children write routinely for a range of tasks, purposes, and audiences.

Name _____

DIRECTIONS Choose a word from below and draw it in the box. Then write a sentence using the word.

ruined   aisles

Responses will vary.

Write in Response to Reading

DIRECTIONS Complete the sentences.

The soccer team wants to use their money to

Responses will vary but should include that they want to fix another team's soccer field.

Hunter wants to use his money to Responses will vary but should include that he wants to buy a skateboard.

Children demonstrate contextual understanding of Benchmark Vocabulary. Children read text closely and use text evidence in their written answers.

Name _____

DIRECTIONS Think about the characters' decisions in *The Winners' Choice* and *Hunter's Money Jar*. Draw pictures to show how their decisions are different.

The Winners' Choice

Children's drawings will vary but should show that the team decides to fix a soccer field.

Hunter's Money Jar

Children's drawings will vary but should show that Hunter decides to save his money.

Children analyze and respond to literary texts.

Name _____

DIRECTIONS Circle the correct word to join the sentences.

Hunter could buy the skateboard, (so /(or)) he could keep saving his money.

Writing

DIRECTIONS Think about the mistakes you circled. Write your edited story on the lines.

Responses will vary.

Children practice various conventions of standard English. Children write routinely for a range of tasks, purposes, and audiences.

Name _____

DIRECTIONS Circle the word for each picture.

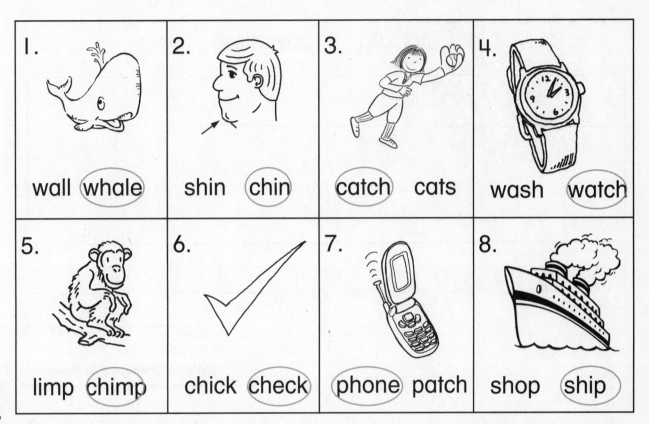

1.	2.	3.	4.
wall (whale)	shin (chin)	(catch) cats	wash (watch)
5.	6.	7.	8.
limp (chimp)	chick (check)	(phone) patch	shop (ship)

Pick a word to finish each sentence.
Write the word on the line.

graph   grass

9. Jim made a mistake on his _____**graph**_____.

what   want

10. He did not know _____**what**_____ to do.

Children apply grade-level phonics and
word analysis skills.

Name _____

DIRECTIONS Choose a word from below and draw it in the box. Then write a sentence using the word.

stacked   adventure

```
┌─────────────────────────────────────────┐
│                                           │
│                                           │
│                                           │
│                                           │
│                                           │
└─────────────────────────────────────────┘
```

_____

Responses will vary.

Write in Response to Reading

How does Patricia feel at the end of *The Winners' Choice*?

Responses may vary but should include that she feels proud.

How does Hunter feel at the end of *Hunter's Money Jar*?

Responses may vary but should include that he feels happy.

Children demonstrate contextual understanding of Benchmark Vocabulary. Children read text closely and use text evidence in their written answers.

Name _____

Cook Up a Surprise

"Mom," said Amy. "Next week is Ms. Carter's birthday. She likes flowers and dogs and cooking. What surprise can our class make?"

Mom had the best idea. The next day, Amy told everyone. "That's a great idea!" they said.

The next Tuesday was Ms. Carter's birthday. After lunch, Amy raised her hand. Then the whole class said, "Happy birthday, Ms. Carter!"

Luis handed Ms. Carter a big book. On the front was a drawing by Jane. It showed a colorful fruit salad. The title of the book was "Our Best Recipes."

Ms. Carter opened the book. She saw a recipe on each page. There were recipes for many things. The children had gotten recipes from their parents. The recipes were for their favorite foods. They had put them in the book and drawn pictures.

"This is a wonderful surprise," said Ms. Carter. "I'll treasure it forever."

Children read text closely to determine what the text says.

Name _____

Look for Clues

On page 187, find details that tell what Ms. Carter likes. Underline the details. Then circle the detail you underlined that gave Amy's mom an idea.

Children should underline *flowers*, *dogs*, and *cooking*. Children should circle *cooking*.

Ask Questions

When she opens the book, what might Ms. Carter ask the students? Write a question.

Possible responses: Where did you get the recipes? Why did you pick these recipes?

Make Your Case

The students work together to make Ms. Carter a surprise birthday gift. Write a sentence to tell how they feel about Ms. Carter.

Possible response: The students really like Ms. Carter.

Children read text closely to determine what the text says.

Name _____

DIRECTIONS Complete each sentence with one of the words in the box.

this	these

_____

I have _____ these _____ coins.

_____

I like _____ this _____ skateboard.

DIRECTIONS Think about your story. Write a sentence that tells your favorite part.

_____

Responses will vary.

_____

_____

_____

_____

_____

_____

Children practice various conventions of standard English. Children write routinely for a range of tasks, purposes, and audiences.

Name _____

DIRECTIONS Write the letters to make a word in each sentence. Then read the story.

R__o__s__e__ wanted to make soup.

She did not have a b__o__n__e__.

So she put a big st__o__n__e__ in the pot.

She did not have a st__o__v__e__.

She made a fire outside her h__o__m__e__.

She hung the pot on a p__o__l__e__.

"I h__o__p__e__ this will be good," Rose said.

Circle the words that have the same long **o** sound as .

(clove)   bond   not   (poke)   stop   (spoke)

drop   lost   (vote)   son   color   (told)

Children apply grade-level phonics and word analysis skills.

Name _____

DIRECTIONS Choose a word below to draw in the box. Then write a sentence using the word.

goods   services

_____

Responses will vary.

- -

_____

Write in Response to Reading

DIRECTIONS Complete the sentence.

Two goods I use are _____

and **Possible responses: food,**

toys, books, clothes

Children demonstrate contextual understanding of Benchmark Vocabulary. Children read text closely and use text evidence in their written answers.

Name _____

DIRECTIONS Circle the pronoun. Use it in a sentence.

Taxes pay for services (everyone) uses.

Possible response: Everyone

helps pay taxes.

Are goods or services more important?
Write your opinion below.

I think _____ goods/services _____ are more

important than _____ goods/services _____ .

Draw a picture of your opinion.

Children practice various conventions of standard English. Children write routinely for a range of tasks, purposes, and audiences.

Lesson 2

Benchmark Vocabulary

Name _____

DIRECTIONS Choose a word below to draw in the box. Then write a sentence using the word.

want   need

Responses will vary.

Write in Response to Reading

DIRECTIONS Complete the sentences.

Jenna buys a _____ bike _____.

She is a _____ consumer _____.

(producer/consumer)

Children demonstrate contextual understanding of Benchmark Vocabulary. Children read text closely and use text evidence in their written answers.

Name _____

DIRECTIONS Circle the proper nouns.
Underline the common nouns.

My school is Roosevelt Elementary.

Sesame Avenue is the only street without a stoplight.

DIRECTIONS Write your supporting reasons below.

I think **goods/services** are more important

because **Responses will vary.**

Children practice various conventions of standard
English. Children write routinely for a range of tasks,
purposes, and audiences.

Name _____

DIRECTIONS Read each sentence.
Write the contraction for the underlined words.

1. "I <u>can not</u> make a nest," said
   the little bird.

   can't

2. "<u>I will</u> need help with the sticks,"
   said the little bird.

   I'll

3. "I <u>do not</u> think I can help," said
   the frog.

   don't

4. "<u>You will</u> need a big bird to help you,"
   said the frog.

   You'll

5. "<u>I am</u> a big bird! I can help," said
   the big bird.

   I'm

Children apply grade-level phonics and word
analysis skills.

DIRECTIONS Choose a word below to draw in the box. Then write a sentence using the word.

collects   taxes

[box for drawing]

Responses will vary.

DIRECTIONS Complete the sentence.

The government collects **taxes.**

List two services the taxes pay for.

Possible responses: police officers, firefighters, parks, schools, libraries

Children demonstrate contextual understanding of Benchmark Vocabulary. Children read text closely and use text evidence in their written answers.

Name _____

DIRECTIONS Circle the word that has an **-s** ending added to the root word.

(drops)   bass   gross

DIRECTIONS Write your opinion about one of the sections in the text. Then write a reason that supports your opinion.

My Opinion: Responses will vary.

My Reason: Responses will vary.

Children practice various conventions of standard English. Children write routinely for a range of tasks, purposes, and audiences.

Name _____

DIRECTIONS Choose a word below to draw in the box. Then write a sentence using the word.

supermarket   necessary   shoppers

_____

Responses will vary.

_____

_____

Write in Response to Reading

DIRECTIONS Complete the sentence.

A supermarket has _____

and Responses will vary but should include

sections or foods in the supermarket.

Children demonstrate contextual understanding of Benchmark Vocabulary. Children read text closely and use text evidence in their written answers.

Name _____

DIRECTIONS Circle the word that makes sense.

That truck is (big / (bigger)) than this truck.

Today is the (warmer / (warmest)) day of the year!

DIRECTIONS List opinion words about a food you like or dislike. Draw a picture of the food.

Opinion words: **Responses will vary.**

_____

_____

_____

_____

Children practice various conventions of standard English. Children write routinely for a range of tasks, purposes, and audiences.

Name _____

DIRECTIONS Choose a word below to draw in the box. Then write a sentence using the word.

producers   farmers   decisions

_____
_____
_____
_____
_____
_____

Responses will vary. _____

- -

_____

Write in Response to Reading

DIRECTIONS Complete the sentence.

_____
- -

If I had a farm, I would grow _____
_____

because Responses will vary but

should include a real fruit, grain,

or vegetable and a reason why.

 Children demonstrate contextual understanding of Benchmark Vocabulary. Children read text closely and use text evidence in their written answers.

Name _____

DIRECTIONS Draw a picture of a producer and consumer from *Goods and Services*. Label your drawing.

> **Drawings will very but should show an example from *Goods and Services*.**

Draw a picture of a producer and consumer from *Supermarket*. Label your drawing.

> **Drawings will very but should show an example from *Supermarket*.**

Discuss with a partner how your pictures are similar and different.

Responses will vary.

 Children analyze and respond to informational text.

Name _____

DIRECTIONS Circle the word that makes sense.

Put the food in (your / you) cart.

Kate wants to get (her / she) favorite fruit.

DIRECTIONS Use the words from Lesson 4 to write an opinion statement and supporting reason about your favorite food.

Responses will vary.

_____

_____

_____

_____

_____

_____

_____

_____

_____

Children practice various conventions of standard English. Children write routinely for a range of tasks, purposes, and audiences.

Name _____

DIRECTIONS Circle the word for each picture.

c**u**be

1. (mule) mile	2. tub (tube)	3. (cub) cube	4. (Pete) pet
5. tug (tune)	6. flat (flute)	7. (tub) tube	8. (hug) huge

Find the word that has the same **long u** sound as ⬭.

Circle the letter.

9. **A.** rut
   B. rid
   (C.) rule

10. **A.** cut
    (B.) cute
    C. cup

Children apply grade-level phonics and word analysis skills.

Name _____

DIRECTIONS Choose a word below to draw in the box. Then write a sentence using the word.

consumers   unpacked

Responses will vary.

Write in Response to Reading

DIRECTIONS Complete the sentence.

Goods and services are alike because they both are

Possible responses: what people buy, things people want, things people need

Children demonstrate contextual understanding of Benchmark Vocabulary. Children read text closely and use text evidence in their written answers.

Name _____

DIRECTIONS Circle the word that makes sense.

Nan (was / were) a customer at the store.

DIRECTIONS Provide a concluding statement for your opinion from Lesson 5.

Responses will vary.

Children practice various conventions of standard English. Children write routinely for a range of tasks, purposes, and audiences.

Name _____

DIRECTIONS Draw a picture of the word.
Write a sentence using the word.

earn

[ ]

Responses will vary.

Write in Response to Reading

What do producers and consumers do?

Producers **Possible response: sell goods and services.**

Consumers **Possible response: buy goods and services.**

 Children demonstrate contextual understanding of Benchmark Vocabulary. Children read text closely and use text evidence in their written answers.

Name _____

DIRECTIONS Circle the word that makes sense.

My mom (buy / (buys)) candy as a treat.

Writing

DIRECTIONS Choose a topic for your opinion piece.
List three topics related to shopping:

1. Topics should be related to

2. shopping, such as favorite

3. stores or things to buy

What topic will you write about?

Responses will vary.

Children practice various conventions of
standard English. Children write routinely for a
range of tasks, purposes, and audiences.

Name _____

DIRECTIONS Pick a word from the box to finish each sentence. Add **-ed** to each word. Write it on the line.

| call | walk | sniff | jump | rest |

1. They ___**jumped**___ rope together.

2. Pam ___**called**___ June.

3. They ___**walked**___ to the park.

4. They ___**rested**___ in the shade.

5. They ___**sniffed**___ the flowers.

Children apply grade-level phonics and word analysis skills.

Name _____

DIRECTIONS Draw the word in the box. Then write a
sentence using the word.

choices

Responses will vary.

Write in Response to Reading

What do producers and consumers do with money?

Producers Possible response: earn
money.

Consumers Possible response: spend
money.

 Children demonstrate contextual understanding of
Benchmark Vocabulary. Children read text closely and
use text evidence in their written answers.

Unit 3 • Module B • Lesson 8 • 209

Name _____

Help Yourself and Others

Have you cleaned out your toy chest or closet lately? You probably have some clothes that are too small. You have toys that you don't play with. Don't keep old clothes and toys. Give them to someone who needs them.

Yesterday I cleaned my closet. I tried on a sweater. Did it shrink? No, I had grown. After I sorted clothes, I looked through toys. There were three games, four stuffed animals, and a train set that I never play with.

Soon I had a pile of clothes and toys. My mom and I put them in bags and took them into town. We put them in a huge bin. Someone will collect the things. Then they'll give them to people who need them.

Giving away unneeded clothes and toys is a great idea. You help others. You recycle valuable things. Everyone should clean out, give away, and recycle!

Children read text closely to determine what the text says.

Name _____

Look for Clues

On page 210, circle words that tell what the family does to help others.

Circled words may vary but could include: give them to people, giving away unneeded clothes and toys

Ask Questions

What questions do you want to ask the writer?

Responses will vary.

Make Your Case

Circle words the writer wants us to think about.

Circled words may include: old clothes and toys, give, away, help, others

Make Your Case: Extend Your Ideas

Write a sentence that tells why it is important to give away what we no longer need.

Responses will vary. Children

should write a sentence such as

It is important because it helps

others and reuses things.

Children read text closely and use text evidence in their written answers.

Name _____

DIRECTIONS Circle the preposition.

She went to Florida (during) the winter.

The campground is (beyond) the trees.

Writing

DIRECTIONS Choose one topic from Lesson 7.
Write an opinion statement.

Topic: Response should be one

topic from Lesson 7.

Opinion Statement

Responses will vary.

Children practice various conventions of standard English. Children write routinely for a range of tasks, purposes, and audiences.

Name _____

DIRECTIONS Choose a word to draw in the box. Then write a sentence using the word.

inventory   spoiled

Responses will vary.

Write in Response to Reading

What happens at the checkout counter?

Possible response: Baggers pack up the groceries.

Children demonstrate contextual understanding of Benchmark Vocabulary. Children read text closely and use text evidence in their written answers.

Name _____

DIRECTIONS Write an end mark at the end of each sentence.

Wow! Look at all that candy!

Watch out!

Writing

DIRECTIONS Write a supporting sentence for your opinion from Lesson 8.

Responses will vary.

Children practice various conventions of standard English. Children write routinely for a range of tasks, purposes, and audiences.

Name _____

DIRECTIONS Choose a word to draw in the box. Then write a sentence using the word.

average   celebrate

Responses will vary.

Write in Response to Reading

DIRECTIONS Complete the sentence.

Supermarkets are important because Possible

response: we buy food there.

Children demonstrate contextual understanding of Benchmark Vocabulary. Children read text closely and use text evidence in their written answers.

Name _____

DIRECTIONS Circle the words that make sense.

Give (to / two / too) sticks of gum (to / two / too) Jen.

Writing

DIRECTIONS Rewrite your opinion statement from Lesson 9 to include a concluding sentence.

Responses will vary.

Children practice various conventions of standard English. Children write routinely for a range of tasks, purposes, and audiences.

Name _____

DIRECTIONS Help the bee get home. Read each word.
Draw a line that goes past only the **long e** words.
Write the **long e** words on the line.

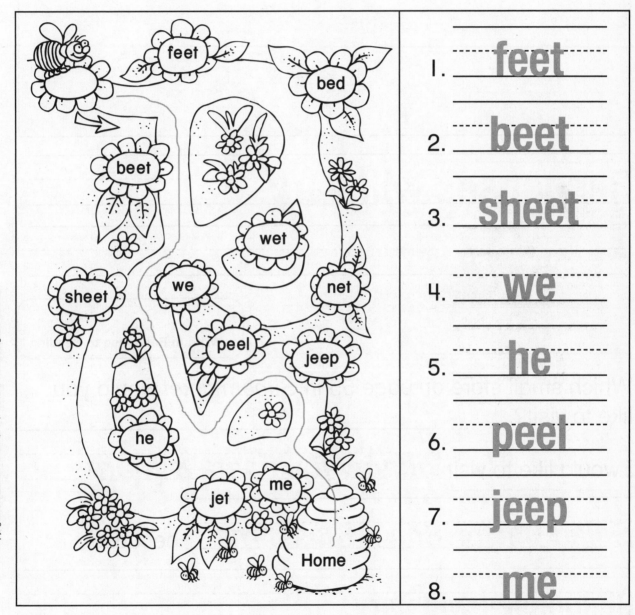

1. feet

2. beet

3. sheet

4. we

5. he

6. peel

7. jeep

8. me

Children apply grade-level phonics and word
analysis skills.

Name _____

Benchmark Vocabulary

DIRECTIONS Choose a word to draw in the box.
Then write a sentence using the word.

goods   services   shoppers

[drawing box]

Responses will vary.

Write in Response to Reading

Which small store on page 55 in *Supermarket* would you like to visit? _____

I would like to visit *Video Villa, Pasta & More,*

Salad Bar, or Bob's Blossoms because

Responses will vary.

Children demonstrate contextual understanding of
Benchmark Vocabulary. Children read text closely and
use text evidence in their written answers.

Name _____

DIRECTIONS Circle the word that has more than one meaning. Draw a picture of both meanings in the box. Write a sentence for each drawing.

The supermarket has (row) after (row) of colors, shapes, and words that shout.

Responses will vary, but picture should show a person rowing a boat and some things lined up in a row.

Example: A person can row a boat. The cans are in a row.

Children analyze and respond to literary and informational text.

Name _____

DIRECTIONS Circle the word that should begin with a capital letter. Then write those words on the lines.

Oranges come from (florida). **Florida**

Popcorn comes from (iowa). **Iowa**

What ideas does your partner have about your writing? Write the ideas below.

Responses will vary.

Children practice various conventions of standard English. Children write routinely for a range of tasks, purposes, and audiences.

Name _____

DIRECTIONS Choose a word to draw in the box. Write a sentence using the word.

producers   consumers   decisions

Responses will vary.

Write in Response to Reading

What are your favorite things to buy at the supermarket? Write your answer as a complete sentence.

Responses will vary.

Children demonstrate contextual understanding of Benchmark Vocabulary. Children read text closely and use text evidence in their written answers.

Name _____

DIRECTIONS Read page 56. Look at the picture. What information do you get from the words? What information do you get from the picture? Draw or write it in the chart.

Words	Picture
Responses will vary but should be information in the words on page	Responses will vary but should be information found in the picture

Children analyze and respond to literary and informational text.

Name _____

DIRECTIONS Circle the action word.
Write the action word to show it happened in the past.

Farmers (pick) fruit. **picked** _____

They (pack) fruit in boxes. **packed** _____

Writing

DIRECTIONS Write your opinion as a blog post.

Responses will vary.

Children practice various conventions of
standard English. Children write routinely for a
range of tasks, purposes, and audiences.

Name _____

ki**tt**en

DIRECTIONS Circle the word for each picture.

1. ramp (rabbit)	2. (button) brake	3. (dinner) dent	4. base (basket)
5. (helmet) hello	6. (mitten) mute	7. mask (muffin)	8. wall (walnut)

Draw a picture for each word.

9. napkin

10. picnic

Drawings will vary.

Children apply grade-level phonics and word analysis skills.

Lesson 1

Phonics

Name _____

DIRECTIONS Circle the word for each picture.

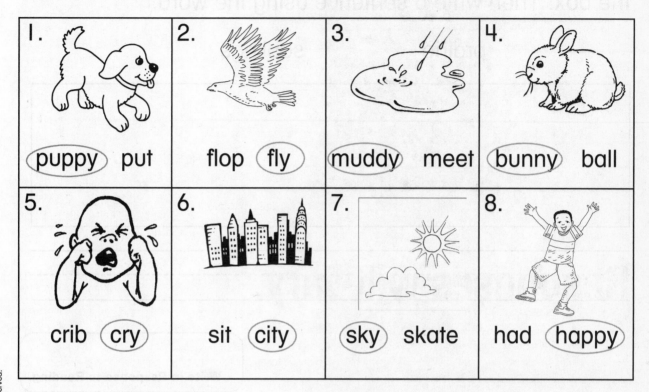

| 1. (puppy) put | 2. flop (fly) | 3. (muddy) meet | 4. (bunny) ball |
| 5. crib (cry) | 6. sit (city) | 7. (sky) skate | 8. had (happy) |

Circle the word to finish each sentence. Write it on the line.

9. I didn't eat dinner, and I am very ___**hungry**___.

         (hungry)   **money**

10. I jumped in the puddle, so my feet

    are not ___**dry**___.

     (dry)   **drip**

 Children apply grade-level phonics and word analysis skills.

Name _____

DIRECTIONS Choose a word from below and draw it in the box. Then write a sentence using the word.

prairie   saplings

Responses will vary.

Write in Response to Reading

DIRECTIONS Write your answer on the lines.

What is Arbor Day?

Responses will vary but should include that it is a day when people plant trees together.

Children demonstrate contextual understanding of Benchmark Vocabulary. Children read text closely and use text evidence in their written answers.

Name _____

DIRECTIONS Circle the verb to complete the sentence.

Today Arbor Day (is / was) a holiday.

Writing

DIRECTIONS Draw a picture of Katie. Then write a sentence about her.

Drawings will vary but should include some details about Katie from the story.

Responses will vary.

Children practice various conventions of standard English.
Children write routinely for a range of tasks, purposes, and audiences.

DIRECTIONS Choose a word from below and draw it in the box. Then write a sentence using the word.

lumber   logs   shade

Responses will vary.

Write in Response to Reading

DIRECTIONS Draw a picture to show what the train brings. Then write a sentence on the lines below that tells one thing it brings.

Responses will vary but should include either *more people* or *lumber.*

Children demonstrate contextual understanding of Benchmark Vocabulary. Children read text closely and use text evidence in their written answers.

DIRECTIONS Circle the word that tells about a noun.

The stores have (big) windows.

The (tall) trees give us shade.

Writing

DIRECTIONS Draw a picture of the setting of *Arbor Day Square.* Then write a sentence to tell about the setting.

Drawings will vary but should show a prairie town.

Possible response: The setting of *Arbor Day Square* is a prairie town.

 Children practice various conventions of standard English. Children write routinely for a range of tasks, purposes, and audiences.

Name _____

DIRECTIONS Circle a word to finish each sentence.
Write it on the line.

He   (Hi)

1. "____**Hi**____," Luke said.

Hi   (He)

2. ____**He**____ is little.

(No)   Nod

3. ____**No**____ one can see him.

(so)   see

4. She is ____**so**____ big.

bed   (be)

5. He will grow to ____**be**____ big too.

Children apply grade-level phonics and word analysis skills.

Name _____

DIRECTIONS Choose a word from below and draw it in the box. Then write a sentence using the word.

town   skips   unload

_____

Responses will vary.

Write in Response to Reading

DIRECTIONS Write your answer on the lines.
Why do the people collect money in a basket?

Responses will vary but should include that they want to buy some trees.

Children demonstrate contextual understanding of Benchmark Vocabulary. Children read text closely and use text evidence in their written answers.

A Mentor for James

James loved school. He loved reading and writing. He loved playing soccer outside. But sometimes James didn't like math. Sometimes adding and subtracting was hard.

"Come after school on Tuesday," Ms. Garcia said. "A student called a mentor will help you."

On Tuesday, James worried about staying after school. Who would his mentor be?

After school, James walked to Room I I I. He saw other first graders working quietly with older students. A girl walked up.

"Hi, James," she said. "I'm Maria, and I'm in fifth grade. I'll help you with math." They sat down, and James showed Maria his math workbook. They talked about each math problem. Maria was very patient.

Maria said their time was up. James was amazed. He had done all his math problems.

"Thanks, Maria. May I come back next week?" James asked.

"Sure," Maria said. "And will you help me with my soccer sometime?"

Children read text closely to determine what the text says.

Name _____

Look for Clues
Draw a box around the word that tells how James feels after he meets Maria. Underline the sentence that tells why James feels that way.

Children draw a box around *amazed.* Children underline
He had done all his math problems.

Ask Questions
Write a question you might ask Maria about being a mentor.

Possible response: How many students do you mentor?

Make Your Case
Retell the story to a partner. Circle a name to finish the sentence: I will tell the story as <u>James Maria</u>.
Write the first sentence of your retelling. Use "I."

Responses will vary but should be from either Maria's or James's point of view.

Children read text closely to determine what the text says.

Name _____

DIRECTIONS Circle the verbs to finish the sentences.

Katie and Papa ((went) / go) to the meeting last week.

The train (come / (came)) yesterday.

Writing

DIRECTIONS Think about the family tradition your story will be about. Write to tell about the tradition.

Responses will vary.

Children practice various conventions of standard English. Children write routinely for a range of tasks, purposes, and audiences.

Name _____

DIRECTIONS Choose a word from below and draw it in the box. Then write a sentence using the word.

parade   soil   neighbors

Responses will vary.

Write in Response to Reading

DIRECTIONS Complete the sentence with two things the people plant.

The people plant _____

Responses will vary but could include maple trees, oak trees, an elm tree, an apple tree, chestnut trees, and a flowering dogwood.

Children demonstrate contextual understanding of Benchmark Vocabulary. Children read text closely and use text evidence in their written answers.

Name _____

DIRECTIONS Write the verb to complete the sentence.

hug   hugs
_____

Papa _____hugs_____ Katie.

Writing

DIRECTIONS Write your story.

Responses will vary.

Children practice various conventions of standard English. Children write routinely for a range of tasks, purposes, and audiences.

Name _____

DIRECTIONS Choose a word from below and draw it in the box. Then write a sentence using the word.

holiday   rakes

Responses will vary.

Write in Response to Reading

DIRECTIONS Write your answer on the lines.
Why do the people want trees?

Responses will vary but could include for climbing, shade, fruit, winter fires, birds, or beauty.

Children demonstrate contextual understanding of Benchmark Vocabulary. Children read text closely and use text evidence in their written answers.

Name _____

DIRECTIONS Rewrite the sentence. Add a detail.

The people gather to plant trees.

_____

- -

Possible response: The happy people gather to plant many apple trees.

_____

- -

_____

Writing

DIRECTIONS Think about details you can add to your story. Rewrite the story below.

_____

Responses will vary.

_____

- -

_____

_____

- -

_____

_____

- -

_____

_____

- -

_____

Children practice various conventions of standard English. Children write routinely for a range of tasks, purposes, and audiences.

Name _____

DIRECTIONS Circle the word for each picture.

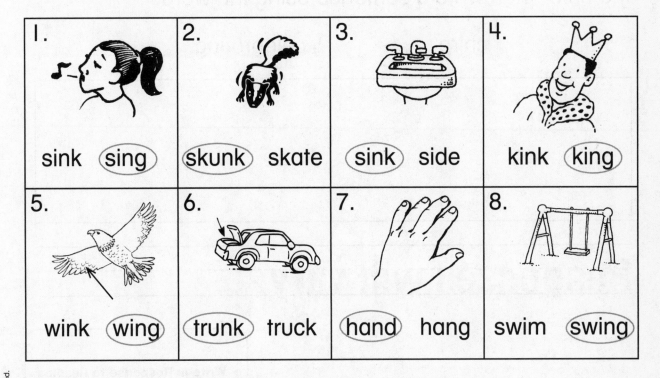

1. sink (sing)	2. (skunk) skate	3. (sink) side	4. kink (king)
5. wink (wing)	6. (trunk) truck	7. (hand) hang	8. swim (swing)

Write the letters **ng** or **nk** to finish the words
for each sentence.

9. Please bri___**ng**___ me a dri___**nk**___.

10. Tha___**nk**___ you for the pretty ri___**ng**___.

Children apply grade-level phonics and word
analysis skills.

Name _____

DIRECTIONS Choose a word from below and draw it in the box. Then write a sentence using the word.

chirp   celebrating

Responses will vary.

DIRECTIONS Draw what the Square looks like now. Then write a sentence on the lines below to tell one way the Square has changed.

Possible response: The trees have grown really tall.

Children demonstrate contextual understanding of Benchmark Vocabulary. Children read text closely and use text evidence in their written answers.

Name _____

DIRECTIONS Write the verb to complete the sentence.

watered   water   will water

They _____ **will water** _____ the trees tomorrow.

DIRECTIONS Think about time and sequence words you can add to your story. Rewrite the story below.

Responses will vary.

_____

_____

_____

_____

_____

_____

_____

_____

_____

_____

_____

Children practice various conventions of standard English. Children write routinely for a range of tasks, purposes, and audiences.

Name _____

DIRECTIONS Choose a word from below and draw it in the box. Then write a sentence using the word.

huge   success

```




```

Responses will vary.

Write in Response to Reading

DIRECTIONS Complete the sentence with two places where Arbor Day is celebrated.

_____

Arbor Day is celebrated in _____

Responses will vary but could

include any of the fifty states or

any of the countries listed on p. 30.

Children demonstrate contextual understanding of Benchmark Vocabulary. Children read text closely and use text evidence in their written answers.

Name _____

DIRECTIONS Write a sentence that tells how the Author's Note and story in *Arbor Day Square* are different.

Possible response: *Arbor Day Square* is a story. It has a beginning, a middle, and an end. It is made up. The Author's Note is informational text. It has a main topic and gives facts that are true.

Children analyze and respond to literary and informational texts.

Name _____

DIRECTIONS Circle the words that need capital letters.

⟨katie⟩ and ⟨megan anne⟩ look at the trees.

DIRECTIONS Think about the mistakes you circled. Write your edited story on the lines.

Responses will vary.

Children practice various conventions of standard English. Children write routinely for a range of tasks, purposes, and audiences.

Name _____

DIRECTIONS Pick a word from the box to finish each compound word. Write it on the line. Draw a line to the picture it matches.

| ball | cakes | pole | set |

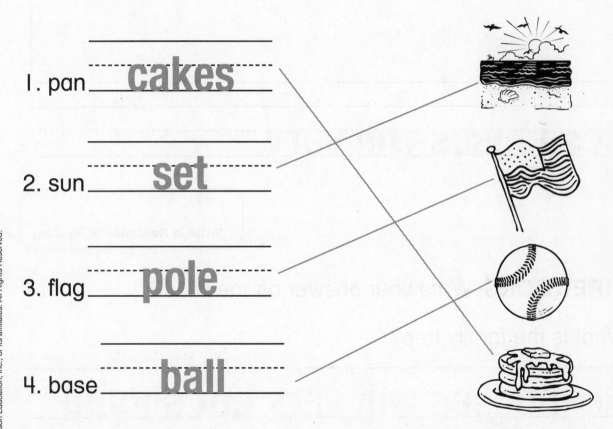

1. pan **cakes** _____

2. sun **set** _____

3. flag **pole** _____

4. base **ball** _____

Find the compound word. Circle the letter.

5. **A.** sandy
   B. sandman
   C. sanding

6. **A.** napkin
   B. happen
   C. dishpan

Children apply grade-level phonics and word analysis skills.

Name _____

DIRECTIONS Choose a word from below and draw it in the box. Then write a sentence using the word.

chopped   pastures   huddled

_____

Responses will vary.

Write in Response to Reading

DIRECTIONS Write your answer on the lines.

What is the family tree?

Responses will vary but should explain that it is a tree that has been in a family's yard for many years.

Children demonstrate contextual understanding of Benchmark Vocabulary. Children read text closely and use text evidence in their written answers.

Name _____

DIRECTIONS Write the past tense form of the verb **stop**.

_____

The boy _____ **stopped** _____ the workers.

DIRECTIONS Think about what might happen after *The Family Tree* ends. Write a story about what happens.

Responses will vary but could include another boy in the family who enjoys swinging on the tree.

_____

_____

_____

_____

_____

_____

_____

Children practice various conventions of standard English. Children write routinely for a range of tasks, purposes, and audiences.

Name _____

DIRECTIONS Draw a picture of the word below in the box. Then write a sentence using the word.

years

Responses will vary.

Write in Response to Reading

DIRECTIONS Write your answer on the lines.

Why does the man leave one tree standing?

Responses will vary.

Children demonstrate contextual understanding of Benchmark Vocabulary. Children read text closely and use text evidence in their written answers.

Name _____

DIRECTIONS Write a question you have about the story. Then write the answer to your question.

Question: Responses will vary.

_____

_____

_____

_____

_____

Answer: Responses will vary.

_____

_____

_____

_____

_____

Children analyze and respond to literary texts.

Name _____

DIRECTIONS Underline the verb in the sentence. Then circle when the action happens.

The man <u>returned</u> with his wife.   (past) now future

Writing

DIRECTIONS Think about changes you can make to your story. Rewrite your story below.

Responses will vary.

_____

- - - - - - - - - - - - - - - -

_____

- - - - - - - - - - - - - - - -

_____

- - - - - - - - - - - - - - - -

_____

- - - - - - - - - - - - - - - -

_____

- - - - - - - - - - - - - - - -

_____

Children practice various conventions of standard English. Children write routinely for a range of tasks, purposes, and audiences.

Name _____

DIRECTIONS Choose a word from below and draw it in the box. Then write a sentence using the word.

widen   protested

[blank box]

_____

Responses will vary.

Write in Response to Reading

DIRECTIONS Write your answer on the lines.

Why does the boy stand in front of the tree?

Responses will vary but should
include that he doesn't want
workers to cut the tree down.

 Children demonstrate contextual understanding of Benchmark Vocabulary. Children read text closely and use text evidence in their written answers.

Name _____

DIRECTIONS Circle the verb to finish the sentence.

Yesterday the boy (is / (was)) sad.

DIRECTIONS Think about details you can add to your event. Rewrite the event below.

Responses will vary.

Children practice various conventions of standard English. Children write routinely for a range of tasks, purposes, and audiences.

Name _____

DIRECTIONS Add the ending.
Write the new word on the line.

Word	Ending	New Word
1. mix	+ -es	mixes
2. brush	+ -es	brushes
3. glass	+ -es	glasses
4. catch	+ -es	catches
5. dress	+ -es	dresses
6. bus	+ -es	buses
7. dish	+ -es	dishes
8. fox	+ -es	foxes
9. pass	+ -es	passes
10. patch	+ -es	patches

Children apply grade-level phonics and word
analysis skills.

Name _____

DIRECTIONS Draw a picture of the word below in the box. Then write a sentence using the word.

assistance

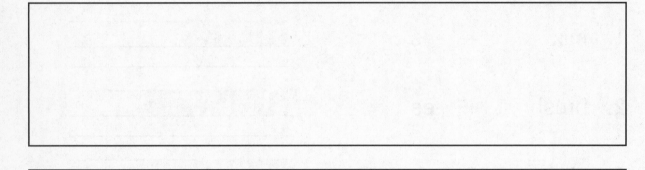

Responses will vary.

Write in Response to Reading

DIRECTIONS Write your answer on the lines.

What is the workers' new plan?

Responses will vary but should include that they build the road around the tree.

Copyright © Pearson Education, Inc., or its affiliates. All Rights Reserved.

Children demonstrate contextual understanding of Benchmark Vocabulary. Children read text closely and use text evidence in their written answers.

Name _____

DIRECTIONS Write your answers on the lines.

What is the big idea of the story?

Responses will vary but should be about family.

What is one thing you learn about the big idea from the details in the story?

Responses will vary but should tell something they learned about family.

Children analyze and respond to literary texts.

Name _____

DIRECTIONS Fill in the right pronoun for the underlined noun.

The young <u>man</u> chopped down trees.

_____

____He____ built a house.

DIRECTIONS Check the items your partner did in the story. Write one change your partner should make.

Revising Checklist

☐ The events are in the right order.

☐ The writer uses time-order words.

☐ The events focus on one topic.

☐ Details tell about each event.

A change I think the writer should make:

_____

Responses will vary.

- -

_____

- -

- -

_____

Children practice various conventions of standard English. Children write routinely for a range of tasks, purposes, and audiences.

Name _____

DIRECTIONS Choose a word from below and draw it in the box. Then write a sentence using the word.

special   alone

Responses will vary.

Write in Response to Reading

What is one thing that Katie does?

Responses will vary but should be based on details in *Arbor Day Square*.

What is one thing that the boy does?

Responses will vary but should be based on details in *The Family Tree*.

Children demonstrate contextual understanding of Benchmark Vocabulary. Children read text closely and use text evidence in their written answers.

DIRECTIONS Fill in the right pronoun for the underlined noun.

The <u>neighbors</u> dance.

The moon shines on _____  _____.

DIRECTIONS Write an ending for your story.

Responses will vary.

Children practice various conventions of standard English. Children write routinely for a range of tasks, purposes, and audiences.

Name _____

DIRECTIONS Circle the word for each picture.

st**or**m

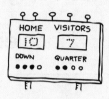

sc**ore**

1. (fork) flick	2. hen (horn)	3. (core) conk	4. (store) stock
5. con (corn)	6. (shorts) shots	7. port (pot)	8. (thorn) tone

Find the word that has the same middle sound as .
Circle the letter.

9. **(A.)** porch
    B. poke
    C. pole

10. **A.** such
    B. shut
    (C.) shore

Children apply grade-level phonics and word
analysis skills.

Name _____

DIRECTIONS Draw a picture of the word below in the box. Then write a sentence using the word.

celebrating

Responses will vary.

Write in Response to Reading

DIRECTIONS Complete the sentences.

One thing I learned in *Arbor Day Square* is

Responses will vary.

One thing I learned in *The Family Tree* is

Responses will vary.

Children demonstrate contextual understanding of Benchmark Vocabulary. Children read text closely and use text evidence in their written answers.

Let's Build a Park!

Luis and his family live in a house in the city. They have a small yard. There is no place to play ball or swing or slide. So Luis's family and their neighbors built a park. Here's how.

First, they picked a spot. Near Luis's house was a big, empty lot with concrete and weeds. It would be perfect! Next, the neighbors planned the park. Would it have a ball field and a playground? Would it have picnic tables?

Next, the neighbors went to their city leaders. They talked about their plan. The leaders voted yes. They gave them some money. The neighbors raised money too. They had a block party and sold food.

The neighbors built the park. Mr. Nuñez planted grass. Mr. Johnson built tables.

Mrs. Parker's company donated swings and slides.

Now Luis's neighborhood has a great place to play, rest, and eat.

Children read text closely to determine what the text says.

Look for Clues

Circle words that tell what the neighbors planted, built, and donated for the new park.

Children should circle grass, tables, swings, and slides.

Ask Questions

Write two questions that city leaders might ask the neighbors.

_____

Responses will vary but should include text

evidence about the neighbors' plan for the

park, such as What will you put in your park?

_____

_____

Ask Questions: Extend Your Ideas

Suppose the leaders ask the neighbors why they need a park. Underline the sentence in the story that will answer the question.

Children should underline There is no place to play ball or swing or slide.

Make Your Case

Circle the word that tells what neighbors can do on the swings and slides. Underline the word that tells what they can do on the grass. Box the word that tells what neighbors can do at the tables.

Children should circle play, underline rest, and box eat.

Children read text closely to determine what the text says.

Name _____

DIRECTIONS Write the sentences.
Use pronouns for the underlined nouns.

<u>Katie</u> spreads a blanket.

She spreads a blanket.

<u>The neighbors</u> have a picnic.

They have a picnic.

DIRECTIONS How will you publish and share your story?
Write your plan.

Responses will vary.

Children practice various conventions of
standard English. Children write routinely for a
range of tasks, purposes, and audiences.

DIRECTIONS Add **-ed** and **-ing** to each word.
Write the new words on the lines.

	Add -ed	**Add -ing**
1. nap	napped	napping
2. pat	patted	patting
3. nod	nodded	nodding
4. jog	jogged	jogging
5. wag	wagged	wagging
6. stop	stopped	stopping
7. pet	petted	petting
8. drop	dropped	dropping
9. clap	clapped	clapping
10. plan	planned	planning

Children apply grade-level phonics and word
analysis skills.

Name _____

DIRECTIONS Choose a word from below and draw it in the box. Then write a sentence using the word.

sunlight   warmth

[Box for drawing]

_____

Responses will vary.

Write in Response to Reading

DIRECTIONS Write your answer on the lines.

What do apple seeds need?

Apple seeds need water,

sunlight, soil, and warmth.

_____

_____

Children demonstrate contextual understanding of Benchmark Vocabulary. Children read text closely and use text evidence in their written answers.

Unit 4 • Module B • Lesson 1 • 265

Name _____

DIRECTIONS Circle the nouns that name more than one.

trunk   (trunks)   blossom   (blossoms)

DIRECTIONS Name the topic of *The Life Cycle of an Apple Tree.* Write one fact about that topic.

Topic: **Possible response: The topic is the life cycle of an apple tree.**

Fact: **Responses should be from the text.**

Children practice various conventions of standard English. Children write routinely for a range of tasks, purposes, and audiences.

Name _____

DIRECTIONS Choose a word from below and draw it in the box. Then write a sentence using the word.

cover   form

Responses will vary.

Write in Response to Reading

DIRECTIONS Write the heading of your favorite part of the book. Write why you like that part.

Possible responses: Apple Seeds, Growing, Apples!, Starting Over, How Apple Trees Grow; response should explain why.

 Children demonstrate contextual understanding of Benchmark Vocabulary. Children read text closely and use text evidence in their written answers.

Name _____

DIRECTIONS Write a heading from the text. Draw a picture to show something you learned from that section.

_____
- -
_____

_____
- -
_____

What I Learned:

Children should choose and write a heading from the text and draw a picture to show a detail from that section of the text.

Children analyze and respond to informational text.

Name _____

DIRECTIONS Circle the nouns that name more than one.

fox (foxes) peach (peaches)

(wishes) wish bus (buses)

DIRECTIONS Write one science word from the class picture dictionary. Write what the word means. Draw a picture of the word.

Word: _____

Definition: _____

Responses should be a science
word and its meaning.

Children practice various conventions of standard English. Children write routinely for a range of tasks, purposes, and audiences.

Name _____

DIRECTIONS Circle the word for each picture.

f<u>ar</u>m

1.	2.	3.	4.
(arm) am	band (barn)	core (car)	jar (jam)

5.	6.	7.	8.
duck (dark)	(party) patty	(cart) cork	cord (card)

Find the word that rhymes with .
Circle the letter.

9. **A.** form
    B. (far)
    C. for

10. **A.** (tar)
     B. torn
     C. trap

Children apply grade-level phonics and word analysis skills.

Name _____

DIRECTIONS Choose a word from below and draw it in the box. Then write a sentence using the word.

picked   ground   rot

Responses will vary.

Write in Response to Reading

DIRECTIONS Complete the sentence.

A ripe apple is Possible responses: red, ready to be picked, ready to eat.

Children demonstrate contextual understanding of Benchmark Vocabulary. Children read text closely and use text evidence in their written answers.

DIRECTIONS Circle the nouns in this sentence.

The (seeds) in an (apple) can become a (tree).

DIRECTIONS Write a sentence to answer the question.

Where do apple seeds come from?

Possible response: Apple seeds
come from inside apples.

Children practice various conventions of standard English. Children write routinely for a range of tasks, purposes, and audiences.

Name _____

DIRECTIONS Choose a word from below and draw it in the box. Then write a sentence using the word.

cycle   continues

```
┌─────────────────────────────────────┐
│                                      │
│                                      │
│                                      │
│                                      │
│                                      │
└─────────────────────────────────────┘
```

Responses will vary.

Write in Response to Reading

DIRECTIONS Circle the word or words to show your opinion. Then complete the sentence.

I like / don't like the diagram because Possible

responses: it is easy to read,

it leaves parts out.

Children demonstrate contextual understanding of Benchmark Vocabulary. Children read text closely and use text evidence in their written answers.

Name _____

DIRECTIONS Draw a line to match the noun with the correct verb.

The seed   sprout.

The seeds   sprouts.

DIRECTIONS Draw detailed pictures showing the sequence of steps for how to brush your teeth.

Drawing of toothpaste on toothbrush.	**Drawing of brushing each tooth.**
Drawing of spitting out toothpaste.	**Drawing of rinsing toothbrush.**

Children practice various conventions of standard English. Children write routinely for a range of tasks, purposes, and audiences.

Name _____

DIRECTIONS Draw the word below in the box. Then write a sentence using the word.

grow

```
┌─────────────────────────────────────────────┐
│                                             │
│                                             │
│                                             │
│                                             │
│                                             │
└─────────────────────────────────────────────┘
```

Responses will vary.

Write in Response to Reading

DIRECTIONS Write your answer on the lines below.

How are the words *sprout* and *grow* connected?

Possible responses: one happens after the other; a seed sprouts, and then a plant begins to grow.

Children demonstrate contextual understanding of Benchmark Vocabulary. Children read text closely and use text evidence in their written answers.

DIRECTIONS Read the words in the box. Write two sentences that show how some words are connected.

soil	branches	leaves	water
trunk	warmth	sunlight	blossoms

1. words that name parts of an apple tree

Possible response: Branches, leaves, trunk, and blossoms name parts of an apple tree.

2. words that name things an apple tree needs to grow

Possible response: Apple trees need soil, water, warmth, and sunlight to grow.

Children analyze and respond to informational text.

Name _____

DIRECTIONS Circle the word that tells that the action happens now.

The seed (grows) into a plant.

Some apples (fall) from the trees.

DIRECTIONS Write the first step for how to brush your teeth.

Responses will vary but could include putting toothpaste on your toothbrush.

Children practice various conventions of standard English. Children write routinely for a range of tasks, purposes, and audiences.

Name _____

DIRECTIONS Circle the word for each picture.

 h**er**

 b**ir**d

 s**ur**f

1.  short (shirt)	2.  (clerk) click	3. (curl) chill	4.  barn (burn)
5.  (fern) fan	6.  (skirt) skit	7.  fist (first)	8.  (stir) store

Find the word that has the same vowel sound as .
Circle the letter.

9. **A.** hard
    B. hut
    (C.) hurt

10. **A.** torn
    (B.) turn
    C. tune

Children apply grade-level phonics and word analysis skills.

DIRECTIONS Choose a word from below and draw it in the box. Then write a sentence using the word.

someday   bottom

Responses will vary.

Write in Response to Reading

Would you like to plant an oak tree seed?
Write to tell why or why not.

Possible responses: Yes, because over time it would grow into an oak tree. No, because it would take too long for it to grow into an oak tree.

 Children demonstrate contextual understanding of Benchmark Vocabulary. Children read text closely and use text evidence in their written answers.

Unit 4 • Module B • Lesson 6 • 279

Name _____

DIRECTIONS Circle the words that tell something will happen in the future.

The seed (will grow) into a bean plant.

The leaves (will cover) the tree.

Writing

DIRECTIONS Recall information from experiences to add a fact to your writing from Lesson 5.

Possible response: It is also a good idea to floss your teeth.

Children practice various conventions of standard English. Children write routinely for a range of tasks, purposes, and audiences.

Name _____

DIRECTIONS Choose a word from below and draw it in the box. Then write a sentence using the word.

sunlight   warmth

Responses will vary.

Write in Response to Reading

DIRECTIONS Write your answer on the lines below.

What can you find inside apples?

Possible response: You can find tiny apple seeds inside apples.

Children demonstrate contextual understanding of Benchmark Vocabulary. Children read text closely and use text evidence in their written answers.

DIRECTIONS Write **is** or **are** to complete the sentences.

A tree _____**is**_____ a large plant.

The seeds _____**are**_____ in the apple.

DIRECTIONS Write a sentence to provide a sense of closure about brushing your teeth.

Possible response: Brushing your teeth is a lot of work, but it is very important.

Children practice various conventions of standard English. Children write routinely for a range of tasks, purposes, and audiences.

Name _____

DIRECTIONS Pick a word from the box that means the same as each pair of words. Write it on the line.

he's	it's	I've	that's	they're
they've	we're	we've	you're	you've

1. I + have I've	2. we + are we're
3. it + is it's	4. that + is that's
5. you + have you've	6. they + have they've
7. we + have we've	8. he + is he's
9. they + are they're	10. you + are you're

Children apply grade-level phonics and word analysis skills.

Name _____

DIRECTIONS Choose a word below and draw it in the box. Then write a sentence using the word.

sprinkle   carefully   soaks

Responses will vary.

Write in Response to Reading

Pick a picture from the text. Explain how it shows a key idea in the text.

Responses will vary.

Children demonstrate contextual understanding of Benchmark Vocabulary. Children read text closely and use text evidence in their written answers.

The Best Neighbor Ever

Mrs. Cook is the kindest neighbor ever. Dan's mom got sick, and Mrs. Cook brought dinner. The family's car broke down. Mrs. Cook took Dan to soccer practice. Dan starred in the school play. Mrs. Cook sewed his costume.

One day, Dan said, "How can I help Mrs. Cook? I can't cook or drive or sew."

"You could carry her groceries," Mom said.

"She shops when I'm at school," Dan said.

"You could pick up her newspaper," Mom said.

"She gets it while I'm sleeping," Dan said.

"You could share some of our cake," Mom said.

"She never eats sweets," Dan said.

They looked outside. Mrs. Cook was raking autumn leaves into a big pile. Dan and Mom smiled. Dan put on his jacket. He grabbed a rake and ran next door.

Later, Mrs. Cook looked at the piles of leaves. "You made a bigger pile than I did, Dan. You're the best neighbor ever."

Children read text closely to determine what the text says.

Look for Clues

Circle the last sentence in the story. Underline the words at the beginning of the story that connect to the last sentence.

Ask Questions

Why does Mrs. Cook help Dan and his family?

Responses should use evidence from the text.

Make Your Case

Circle the name of the person who is the best neighbor in the story. **Possible responses: Mrs. Cook, Dan**

Make Your Case: Extend Your Ideas

On a sheet of paper, draw a picture of the best neighbor helping. Write words to describe how he or she is helping.

Responses will vary but should show a character from the story and a sentence or phrase to describe what the character is doing to help.

Children read text closely and use text evidence in their written answers.

Name _____

DIRECTIONS Does the verb match the noun?
Circle yes or no.

Trees grow from seeds. (Yes)/No

A seed grow into a plant. Yes/(No)

Writing

DIRECTIONS Go back to your writing from Lessons 4, 5, and 6. Add sequence words. Rewrite one step with a time-order word on the lines below.

Possible responses: First, put toothpaste on toothbrush. Now, brush each tooth. Next, spit out toothpaste.

Children practice various conventions of standard English. Children write routinely for a range of tasks, purposes, and audiences.

Name _____

Benchmark Vocabulary

DIRECTIONS Choose a word from below and draw it in the box. Then write a sentence using the word.

different   loose

Responses will vary.

Write in Response to Reading

DIRECTIONS Complete the sentence.

The text tells how a bean seed grows to be a

Possible Responses: plant; bean

plant; bean shoot

Children demonstrate contextual understanding of Benchmark Vocabulary. Children read text closely and use text evidence in their written answers.

Name _____

DIRECTIONS Write a complete sentence that tells something about seeds.

Responses will vary but should be a declarative sentence about seeds.

Writing

DIRECTIONS Write about one revision from your peer review.

Responses should be about one way children will revise their writing.

Children practice various conventions of standard English. Children write routinely for a range of tasks, purposes, and audiences.

Name _____

DIRECTIONS Draw the word below in the box. Then write a sentence using the word.

needs

Responses will vary.

Write in Response to Reading

DIRECTIONS Write your answer on the lines. When you plant bean seeds, why should you put them in sunlight?

Possible response: Bean plants need the sun to grow.

Children demonstrate contextual understanding of Benchmark Vocabulary. Children read text closely and use text evidence in their written answers.

Name _____

DIRECTIONS Add the correct end mark to the sentence.

An oak tree grows slowly _____.

DIRECTIONS Use *How a Seed Grows* and *The Life Cycle of an Apple Tree* to answer the question. Use a complete sentence.

What does a seed need to grow?

Possible response: A seed needs soil, water, and sun to grow.

Children practice various conventions of standard English. Children write routinely for a range of tasks, purposes, and audiences.

Name _____

DIRECTIONS Circle the word for each picture.

small   smal**ler**   smal**lest**

I.  (faster) fastest	2.  bigger (biggest)	3.  (taller) tallest
4.  sweeter (sweetest)	5. 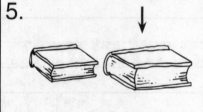 (thicker) thickest	6. 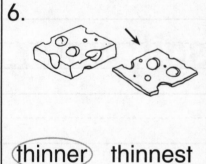 (thinner) thinnest

Write **-er** or **-est** to finish the word in each sentence.

7. The little bird has the few _____est_____ eggs.

8. The little bird has a long _____er_____ tail than the big bird.

Children apply grade-level phonics and word analysis skills.

Name _____

DIRECTIONS Choose a word from below and draw it in the box. Then write a sentence using the word.

conditions   best   worst

Responses will vary.

Write in Response to Reading

DIRECTIONS Look at the last page of *How a Seed Grows.*

Choose a step from the list. What number is it?

Responses will vary.

Draw a picture of what happens at this step.

Drawings should show what is happening during one of the numbered steps from the experiment.

Children demonstrate contextual understanding of Benchmark Vocabulary. Children read text closely and use text evidence in their written answers.

DIRECTIONS Use the last page of *How a Seed Grows* to answer the questions.

1. What do you put the cress seeds on?

   cotton balls or tissue paper

   Circle the text feature where you found the answer.

   paragraph   materials   (numbered list)

2. What question do you have about the experiment?

   Responses will vary.

3. Where can you find the answer?

   Possible response: in a

   dictionary, encyclopedia, or

   science book

Children analyze and respond to literary and informational text.

Name _____

DIRECTIONS Write the sentence with the correct end mark.

What kind of seed is this

What kind of seed is this?

DIRECTIONS Use the class research to take notes about the life cycle of a frog.

Possible response: eggs, tadpole, tadpole with legs, froglet, frog

Children practice various conventions of standard English. Children write routinely for a range of tasks, purposes, and audiences.

Name _____

DIRECTIONS Draw the word below in the box. Then write a sentence using the word.

someday

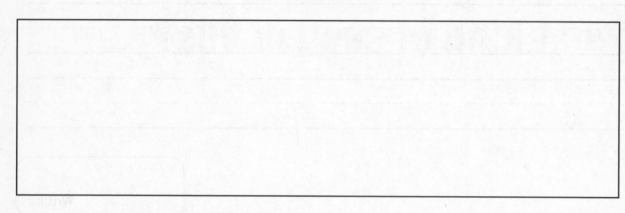

Responses will vary.

Write in Response to Reading

DIRECTIONS Look at page 20 in *How a Seed Grows.*

Why is a drawing better than a photo to show roots growing?

Possible response: A photo will not show the roots because they are under the soil.

Children demonstrate contextual understanding of Benchmark Vocabulary. Children read text closely and use text evidence in their written answers.

Name _____

DIRECTIONS Use complete sentences to answer the questions.

What is shown in the diagram in *The Life Cycle of an Apple Tree?*

The diagram shows the stages in the life cycle of an apple tree.

How are the diagrams in the two texts different?

Possible response: One diagram uses details and drawings instead of photographs.

What do both of these texts have in common?

Possible response: Both of the texts have diagrams of plants and explain how a seed grows.

Children analyze and respond to informational text.

Name _____

DIRECTIONS Write a sentence with the words **in the soil**.

Responses will vary but should include *in the soil*; sentence should be capitalized and use correct end punctuation.

DIRECTIONS Write about the life cycle of a frog.

Possible response: A frog begins as an egg. Then it is a tadpole. It grows legs. It is a froglet. Finally, it becomes a frog.

Children practice various conventions of standard English. Children write routinely for a range of tasks, purposes, and audiences.

Name _____

DIRECTIONS Read each word in the box. Pick a word from the box to finish each sentence. Write it on the line. Read each completed sentence.

fudge	hedge	judge	ledge	smudge

1. Mom made _____ for us to eat.

2. She set it on the _____ .

3. Did it fall into the _____ ?

4. Look, there's a _____ on Bear's face.

5. The _____ thinks Bear ate it too.

Children apply grade-level phonics and word analysis skills.

Name _____

DIRECTIONS Circle the word for each picture.

1. (mail) mall	2. (tray) tree	3. pal (pail)
4. trap (train)	5. he (hay)	6. (pan) pain

Find the word that has the same **long a** sound as ⟨rain⟩ . Circle the letter.

7. **A.** clip

 B. clap

 (C.) clay

8. **A.** man

 (B.) main

 C. mine

Children apply grade-level phonics and word analysis skills.

Name _____

DIRECTIONS Choose a word from below and draw it in the box. Then write a sentence using the word.

brave   secret   sparkly

Responses will vary.

Write in Response to Reading

DIRECTIONS Draw a picture of the moon. Then write words the story uses to tell about the moon.

Drawings should show the moon.

Possible responses: big, bright, round

Children demonstrate contextual understanding of Benchmark Vocabulary. Children read text closely and use text evidence in their written answers.

DIRECTIONS Write a short command.

Responses will vary but should be an imperative sentence with an exclamation mark or a period.

Writing

DIRECTIONS Write to tell about King Kafu.

Possible response: King Kafu said he was brave, but he was afraid of the dark.

Children practice various conventions of standard English. Children write routinely for a range of tasks, purposes, and audiences.

Name _____

DIRECTIONS Choose a word from below and draw it in the box. Then write a sentence using the word.

bragged   peeping

Responses will vary.

Write in Response to Reading

DIRECTIONS Write your answer on the lines.

What is King Kafu's secret?

Responses will vary but should include that he is afraid of the dark.

Children demonstrate contextual understanding of Benchmark Vocabulary. Children read text closely and use text evidence in their written answers.

DIRECTIONS Add an end mark to each sentence.

Look out **[! or .]**

Please turn on the light **[! or .]**

DIRECTIONS Think about the beginning of *King Kafu and the Moon.* Write to tell what happens.

Possible response: King Kafu's night-light doesn't come on, so he uses the light from the

moon so he is not afraid. But he notices that the moon is getting smaller. He thinks part

of the moon is missing.

Children practice various conventions of standard English. Children write routinely for a range of tasks, purposes, and audiences.

Name _____

DIRECTIONS Write each underlined word correctly.
Add the ' where it belongs.

1. <u>Janes</u> drum = _____ Jane's _____ drum

2. <u>dogs</u> bone = _____ dog's _____ bone

3. <u>Moms</u> cup = _____ Mom's _____ cup

4. <u>babys</u> crib = _____ baby's _____ crib

5. <u>pets</u> beds = _____ pets' _____ beds

Pick a word from the box to match each picture.
Write it on the line.

girls'	Matt's

6. _____ Matt's _____ lunch

7. _____ girls' _____ games

Children apply grade-level phonics and word
analysis skills.

Lesson 3

Name _____

Benchmark Vocabulary

DIRECTIONS Choose a word from below and draw it in the box. Then write a sentence using the word.

piece   disappearing   capture

Responses will vary.

Write in Response to Reading

DIRECTIONS Draw a picture of the moon in this part of the story. Then write to tell what happens to the moon.

Drawings should show the moon with part of it missing.

Responses will vary but should include that the moon is disappearing.

 Children demonstrate contextual understanding of Benchmark Vocabulary. Children read text closely and use text evidence in their written answers.

306 • Unit 5 • Module A • Lesson 3

Copyright © Pearson Education, Inc., or its affiliates. All Rights Reserved.

Name _____

Look Out for Wildlife

Wild animals are amazing! They can be scary too! Mom and Dad took me to Yellowstone National Park. Many wild animals live in its fields and woods.

One day we drove through the park. We saw a herd of bison. Another name for bison is buffalo. A bison has shaggy hair and a big bump on its back. We drove on and reached a dead end. Suddenly a huge bear came toward the car. It looked mad!

Dad said, "Don't worry. She can't get in the car." Dad slowly backed up the car. Then we drove away. The huge bear watched us go. My heart was beating fast. But I still took some pictures. They show the mother bear—and its cub! Dad said the bear was just protecting its baby.

Children read text closely to determine what the text says.

Look for Clues

Circle the name of an animal. Underline a detail that tells about the animal. Circle the name of another animal. Underline a detail about the animal. **Responses will vary.**

Ask Questions

Write one thing you would like to know about Yellowstone National Park.

Possible response: What other

animals live there?

Make Your Case

Finish the sentence: Dad backed up to go away from

a huge bear.

Make Your Case: Extend Your Ideas

What was the bear doing? Draw a box around the answer in the story. What might the bear have done if Dad had not backed up?

Responses will vary, but children

should infer that the bear might

have attacked, growled, run at

the car, etc.

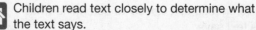

Children read text closely to determine what the text says.

Name _____

DIRECTIONS Write a statement. Then write a question.

Responses will vary but should include a statement with a period and a question with a question mark.

Writing

DIRECTIONS Think about what happens next in the story. Write to tell what happens. Use time-order words.

Possible response: First, King Kafu thinks the moon is disappearing. So he screams. Then,

the guard comes in to see what is wrong. The king shows the guard that part of the moon

is missing. Finally, King Kafu decides to ask the villagers to capture the moon for him.

Children practice various conventions of standard English. Children write routinely for a range of tasks, purposes, and audiences.

Name _____

DIRECTIONS Choose a word from below and draw it in the box. Then write a sentence using the word.

announcement   confused   reward

Responses will vary.

Write in Response to Reading

DIRECTIONS Write your answer on the lines.
What does King Kafu ask the villagers to do?

Responses will vary but should include that he wants them to bring him the moon.

Children demonstrate contextual understanding of Benchmark Vocabulary. Children read text closely and use text evidence in their written answers.

Name _____

DIRECTIONS Write an exclamation.

Responses will vary but should be an exclamatory sentence with an exclamation mark.

Writing

DIRECTIONS Write a plan for your story.

Characters Responses will vary.

_____

Setting _____

_____

Events _____

_____

_____

_____

Children practice various conventions of standard English. Children write routinely for a range of tasks, purposes, and audiences.

DIRECTIONS Choose a word from below and draw it in the box. Then write a sentence using the word.

searched   hiding

Responses will vary.

DIRECTIONS Write your answer on the lines below.

What do the villagers use to help them catch the moon?

Responses will vary but could include fishing rods, butterfly nets, or a rocket.

Children demonstrate contextual understanding of Benchmark Vocabulary. Children read text closely and use text evidence in their written answers.

Name _____

DIRECTIONS Circle the noun that should end with **'s**.

The boy searched the (king) castle.

The (boy) idea was to fill the streets with lights.

DIRECTIONS Think of three events for your story.
Write your plan.

Event 1 Responses will vary. _____

_____

_____

Event 2 _____

_____

_____

Event 3 _____

_____

_____

 Children practice various conventions of
standard English. Children write routinely for a
range of tasks, purposes, and audiences.

Name _____

DIRECTIONS Circle the word for each picture.

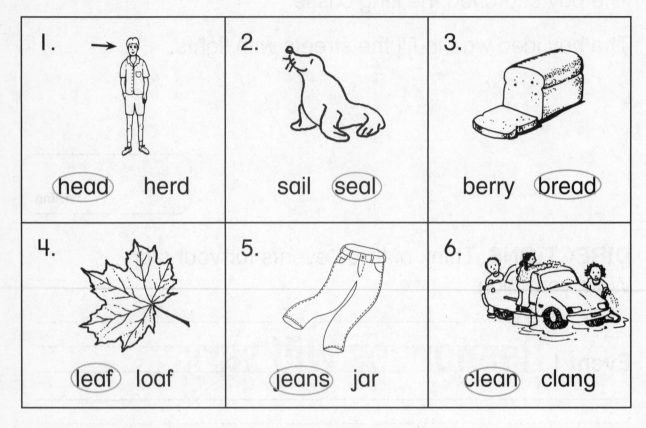

1. (head) herd

2. sail (seal)

3. berry (bread)

4. (leaf) loaf

5. (jeans) jar

6. (clean) clang

Circle the words that finish each sentence.

7. **(Please)/ Place** pass the **(peas)/ bees**.

8. I hit my **(head)/ help** when I fell.

9. I **read / rang** my book at the **(beach)/ birch**.

Children apply grade-level phonics and word analysis skills.

Name _____

DIRECTIONS Choose a word from below and draw it in the box. Then write a sentence using the word.

dizzy   festival

Responses will vary.

Write in Response to Reading

DIRECTIONS Write your answer on the lines.

What do the villagers learn about the moon?

Responses will vary but should be based on text evidence.

Children demonstrate contextual understanding of Benchmark Vocabulary. Children read text closely and use text evidence in their written answers.

Name _____

DIRECTIONS Circle the noun that should end with '.

The (kids) backpacks are in the classroom.

The teacher put the (girls) coats on the hooks.

Writing

DIRECTIONS Think of a conclusion for your story.
Write your plan.

Responses will vary.

Children practice various conventions of standard
English. Children write routinely for a range of tasks,
purposes, and audiences.

Name _____

DIRECTIONS Choose a word from below and draw it in the box. Then write a sentence using the word.

afraid   bright

┌─────────────────────────────────────┐
│   │
│   │
│   │
│   │
└─────────────────────────────────────┘

Responses will vary.

Write in Response to Reading

DIRECTIONS Write a sentence to tell about the ending of *King Kafu and the Moon.*

Responses will vary but should include the festival of light or the boy getting one thousand gold coins.

 Children demonstrate contextual understanding of Benchmark Vocabulary. Children read text closely and use text evidence in their written answers.

Name _____

DIRECTIONS Choose two words or phrases from the story. Write each word or phrase. Then write a sentence with the word or phrase.

Word/Phrase 1: _____

Responses will vary.

Word/Phrase 2: _____

Responses will vary.

Children analyze and respond to literary texts.

Name _____

DIRECTIONS Write the sentence. Add ' or 's to the underlined noun.

The <u>moon</u> light is bright.

The moon's light is bright.

DIRECTIONS Think of sensory words you can add to your story. Write the words.

Responses will vary.

Children practice various conventions of standard English. Children write routinely for a range of tasks, purposes, and audiences.

Name _____

DIRECTIONS Add **-ed** to each word.
Write the new word on the line.

 fr**ied**

1. dry _____ dried

2. copy _____ copied

3. spy _____ spied

4. try _____ tried

Add **-er** and **-est** to each word.
Write the new words on the lines.

	Add -er	Add -est
5. silly	sillier	silliest
6. funny	funnier	funniest
7. happy	happier	happiest
8. easy	easier	easiest

Children apply grade-level phonics and word
analysis skills.

Name _____

DIRECTIONS Draw a picture of the word below in the box. Then write a sentence using the word.

glows

[drawing box   ]

Responses will vary.

Write in Response to Reading

DIRECTIONS Complete the sentence to tell a detail about the moon.

The moon Responses will vary but should be based on text evidence.

Children demonstrate contextual understanding of Benchmark Vocabulary. Children read text closely and use text evidence in their written answers.

Name _____

DIRECTIONS Write a question you have about the text. Then write the answer to your question.

Question: Responses will vary.

_____

_____

_____

_____

_____

_____

Answer: Responses will vary.

_____

_____

_____

_____

_____

Children analyze and respond to informational texts.

DIRECTIONS Rewrite the sentence. Add a detail.

The sun is a star.

_____

Possible response: The bright

sun is a shining star.

DIRECTIONS Write a plan for your story.

_____

Characters **Responses will vary.**

_____

Setting _____

_____

Events _____

_____

_____

_____

Children practice various conventions of standard English. Children write routinely for a range of tasks, purposes, and audiences.

Name _____

DIRECTIONS Choose a word from below and draw it in the box. Then write a sentence using the word.

closer   valleys

Responses will vary.

Write in Response to Reading

DIRECTIONS Write your answer on the lines.

What is one way the moon is like Earth?

Responses will vary but could include that both have mountains, valleys, or craters.

Children demonstrate contextual understanding of Benchmark Vocabulary. Children read text closely and use text evidence in their written answers.

Name _____

DIRECTIONS Add letters to spell words.

_c_at   _b_at   _c_a_k_e   _t_a_m_e

Possible responses shown.

DIRECTIONS Think of two events for your story. Write your plan.

Event 1 Responses will vary.

_____

_____

_____

Event 2 _____

_____

_____

_____

Children practice various conventions of standard English. Children write routinely for a range of tasks, purposes, and audiences.

Name _____

DIRECTIONS Choose a word from below and draw it in the box. Then write a sentence using the word.

smaller   possible   orbit

Responses will vary.

Write in Response to Reading

DIRECTIONS Write your answer on the lines.

What is one interesting fact you learned about the sun, the moon, or Earth?

Responses will vary but should be based on facts and details in the text.

Children demonstrate contextual understanding of Benchmark Vocabulary. Children read text closely and use text evidence in their written answers.

Name _____

DIRECTIONS Write the words. Add **er.** Then write a sentence that uses one of the words.

slow **slower**   fast **faster**

Responses will vary but should use *slower* or *faster* to show a comparison.

Writing

DIRECTIONS Think of a conclusion for your story. Write your plan.

Responses will vary.

Children practice various conventions of standard English. Children write routinely for a range of tasks, purposes, and audiences.

Name _____

DIRECTIONS Circle the word for each picture.

1.	2.	3.
(snow) snap	(road) rod	bee (bow)
4.	5.	6.
sap (soap)	(leaf) loaf	ray (row)

Write the letters that finish the words in each sentence.

7. The g____**oa**____t drank from the b____**ow**____l.

8. They looked high and l____**ow**____, but they could not

find the r____**oa**____d.

Children apply grade-level phonics and word analysis skills.

Name _____

DIRECTIONS Choose a word from below and draw it in the box. Then write a sentence using the word.

crescent   astronauts

Responses will vary.

Write in Response to Reading

DIRECTIONS Write your answer on the lines.
Why can we see the moon?

Responses will vary but should include that the sun's light bounces off of it.

Children demonstrate contextual understanding of Benchmark Vocabulary. Children read text closely and use text evidence in their written answers.

Name _____

DIRECTIONS Write the date correctly.

october 31 2015

October 31, 2015

DIRECTIONS Write details about the moon that you can add to your story.

Responses will vary but could include any of the following: the moon gets its light from

the sun; the sun's light bounces off the moon; we only see the part of the moon that is lit

by the sun; when the moon is a thin strip, it is called a crescent; when it looks like a silver

quarter, it is called a full moon; astronauts walked on the moon in 1969.

Children practice various conventions of standard English. Children write routinely for a range of tasks, purposes, and audiences.

Name _____

DIRECTIONS Choose a word from below and draw it in the box. Then write a sentence using the word.

disappearing   crescent

Responses will vary.

Write in Response to Reading

DIRECTIONS Draw one way the moon can look. Then write a sentence that tells how it looks.

Drawings will vary but should show one of the phases of the moon described in the books.

Responses will vary but should reflect the child's drawing.

Children demonstrate contextual understanding of Benchmark Vocabulary. Children read text closely and use text evidence in their written answers.

Name _____

DIRECTIONS Write your answers on the lines.
First, look at page 25 of *Let's Visit the Moon*.
What does the text say? We see the moon because

sunlight bounces off of it.

Now look at pages 26 and 27. Why do we only see part of
the moon sometimes?

Responses will vary but should include that we

only see the part that the sun's light shines on.

Next, look at pages 8 and 9 of *King Kafu and the Moon*.
What does King Kafu say? King Kafu says the moon is

disappearing.

What is actually happening to the moon?

Responses will vary but should include that the

sun is shining only on a smaller part of the moon.

Children analyze and respond to literary and
informational texts.

Name _____

DIRECTIONS Add **to, too,** or **two** to the sentence.

I would like to go _____**to**_____ the moon.

DIRECTIONS Look over your story. Check off what you have done. Write any new ideas you have.

☐ The sentences in my story tell about visiting the moon.

☐ Each sentence begins with a capital letter.

☐ Each sentence ends with an end mark.

☐ I have checked the spelling of words I wasn't sure of.

Responses will vary.

_____

_____

_____

_____

_____

 Children practice various conventions of standard English. Children write routinely for a range of tasks, purposes, and audiences.

Name _____

DIRECTIONS Circle the word for each picture.

1.	stub ⟨scrub⟩	2.	sting ⟨string⟩
3.	those ⟨three⟩	4.	⟨spring⟩ sing
5.	⟨squeeze⟩ sneeze	6.	⟨stripe⟩ ripe

Write the letters that finish the words in each sentence.

7. She ___thr___ew the ball ___thr___ough

the ___scr___een door.

8. I had a sore ___thr___oat.

Children apply grade-level phonics and word analysis skills.

Name _____

DIRECTIONS Choose a word from below and draw it in the box. Then write a sentence using the word.

hiding   glows

Responses will vary.

Write in Response to Reading

DIRECTIONS Circle the text you like better. Tell why you like it.

I like *King Kafu and the Moon / Let's Visit the Moon* better because

Responses will vary.

Children demonstrate contextual understanding of Benchmark Vocabulary. Children read text closely and use text evidence in their written answers.

Name _____

Is Your Polar Bear Happy?

What would you do with an unhappy elephant? Some scientists study animal behavior. They can answer this question.

Some scientists watch animals in the wild. Others see how people's pets act. Still others watch zoo animals. They see how the animals behave. Is the animal comfortable in its zoo home? Does it eat enough? How does it get along with other animals?

At one zoo, a polar bear seemed upset. He swam up and down his pool all day. Scientists watched the bear for several days. They took notes. They decided to give the bear more toys. They played games with him.

At another zoo, some elephants were causing problems. Scientists watched their behavior. Then they gave the elephants more exercise. They fed them different foods. They put the foods in feeders off the ground. The elephants behaved better.

People don't understand everything about animals. These scientists help us learn more.

Children read text closely to determine what the text says.

Name _____

Look for Clues

Underline sentences that tell about animal behaviors that scientists study. Responses will vary.

Ask Questions

What question would you ask a scientist about how animals behave?

_____

Responses will vary.

_____

Make Your Case

Box words that show what happens when a scientist helps an unhappy animal. Responses will vary.

Make Your Case: Extend Your Ideas

Draw the elephants that were causing problems. Then draw them after the scientists helped them. Write what happened.

Responses should use evidence from the text.

Children read text closely to determine what the text says.

Name _____

DIRECTIONS Add an adjective to the sentence. Then write your own sentence using one or more adjectives.

_____

We saw the _____ moon in the sky.

Responses will vary but should be an adjective that could describe the moon, such as *yellow*, *bright*, or *pale*.

Writing

DIRECTIONS Choose a story to publish. Think of a title for the story. Write the title.

Responses will vary.

_____

_____

_____

Children practice various conventions of standard English. Children write routinely for a range of tasks, purposes, and audiences.

Name _____

DIRECTIONS Circle the word for each picture.

1. (night) note	2. ten (tie)	3. sit (lie)
4. pit (pie)	5. (sit) sight	6. (high) hay

Read the sentences.
Circle the words with the **long i** sound spelled **ie** and **igh**.
Underline the words with the **long e** sound spelled **ie**.

7. I would like another <u>piece</u> of bread.

8. He <u>believes</u> that he is (right.)

9. I am sorry that I (lied) to you.

10. The (sight) of the green <u>field</u> makes us happy.

Children apply grade-level phonics and word
analysis skills.

Name _____

Benchmark Vocabulary

DIRECTIONS Choose a word from below and draw it in the box. Then write a sentence using the word.

planet   space

Responses will vary.

Write in Response to Reading

DIRECTIONS Write your answer on the lines.

What can orbit the sun?

Planets can orbit the sun.

Children demonstrate contextual understanding of Benchmark Vocabulary. Children read text closely and use text evidence in their written answers.

Name _____

DIRECTIONS Write 3 words that end with **-un**.

Possible responses: fun, sun, run

Writing

DIRECTIONS Write 1 or 2 factual sentences about the night sky.

Possible response: The night sky is made of stars and planets.

Children practice various conventions of standard English. Children write routinely for a range of tasks, purposes, and audiences.

Name _____

DIRECTIONS Draw the word below in the box. Then write a sentence using the word.

hotter

Responses will vary.

Write in Response to Reading

Do you like to read about the sun? Tell why or why not.

Responses will vary, but children should give a reason for their opinion.

Children demonstrate contextual understanding of Benchmark Vocabulary. Children read text closely and use text evidence in their written answers.

Name _____

DIRECTIONS Write 3 words that end with **-it.**

Possible responses: sit, lit, hit, fit

DIRECTIONS Draw and label a picture to describe what you have observed about the sun.

Responses will vary but should be about the sun.

Children practice various conventions of standard English. Children write routinely for a range of tasks, purposes, and audiences.

Name _____

DIRECTIONS Circle the word for each picture.

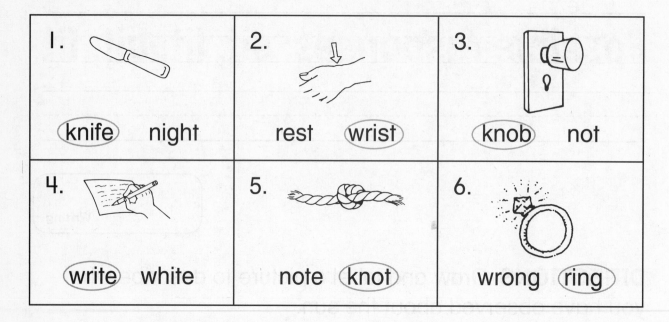

1. (knife)   night

2. rest   (wrist)

3. (knob)   not

4. (write)   white

5. note   (knot)

6. wrong   (ring)

Find the word that has the same beginning sound as the picture.
Circle the letter.

7. (A.) wren

   B. when

   C. went

8. A. sneak

   B. kite

   (C.) knock

Children apply grade-level phonics and word analysis skills.

Name _____

DIRECTIONS Draw the word below in the box. Then write a sentence using the word.

dwarf

Responses will vary.

Write in Response to Reading

DIRECTIONS Write your answer on the lines below.

How can a picture or diagram help you understand the solar system?

Possible response: It can show how far each planet is from the sun.

Children demonstrate contextual understanding of Benchmark Vocabulary. Children read text closely and use text evidence in their written answers.

Name _____

DIRECTIONS Circle the word to complete the sentence.

The (suns / sun's) heat warms Earth.

DIRECTIONS Draw a simple diagram of the sun and planets. Label the parts.

Check children's drawings.

Children practice various conventions of standard English. Children write routinely for a range of tasks, purposes, and audiences.

DIRECTIONS Choose a word from below and draw it in the box. Then write a sentence using the word.

metal   inner

[ ]

Responses will vary.

Write in Response to Reading

Do you like to read about the planets? Why or why not?

Possible response: I like to read about the planets because I want to go into space someday.

Children demonstrate contextual understanding of Benchmark Vocabulary. Children read text closely and use text evidence in their written answers.

Name _____

DIRECTIONS Fill in the word web to figure out what the term *inner planets* means.

Possible responses shown.

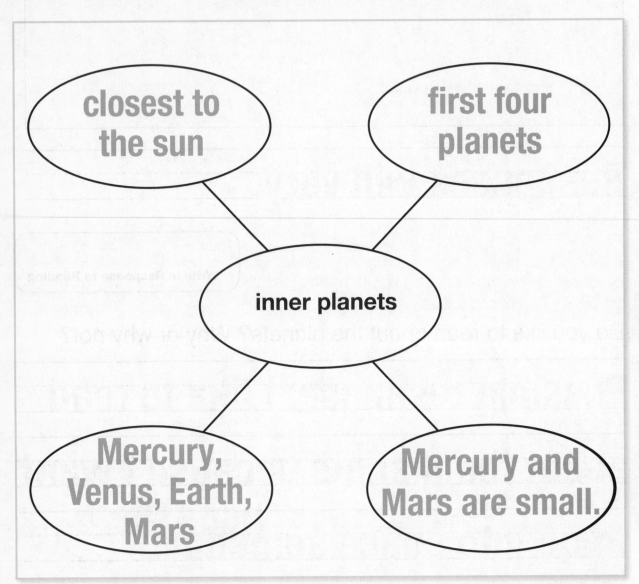

closest to
the sun

first four
planets

inner planets

Mercury,
Venus, Earth,
Mars

Mercury and
Mars are small.

Children analyze and respond to literary and informational text.

Name _____

DIRECTIONS Circle the word in each sentence
that needs a capital letter.
Add an end punctuation mark to each sentence.

(what) is the Earth's closest star **?**

(how) many rings does Saturn have **?**

Writing

DIRECTIONS Research a question about the planets.
Write the answer using a complete sentence.

Question: Possible response: Which
planet is the largest?

Answer: Possible response: The
largest planet is Jupiter.

Copyright © Pearson Education, Inc., or its affiliates. All Rights Reserved.

Children practice various conventions of
standard English. Children write routinely for a
range of tasks, purposes, and audiences.

Name _____

DIRECTIONS Choose a word below and draw it in the box. Then write a sentence using the word.

outer   giant

Responses will vary.

DIRECTIONS Write your answer on the lines below.

What did you learn about Pluto?

Possible responses: Pluto is a dwarf planet. It is much smaller than regular planets. Its orbit is shaped like an egg.

Children demonstrate contextual understanding of Benchmark Vocabulary. Children read text closely and use text evidence in their written answers.

Name _____

DIRECTIONS What did you learn about the giant planets? Draw a picture to show what you know. Write a sentence to tell about your picture.

Responses will vary but should be a drawing of one or more of the giant planets (Jupiter, Saturn, Uranus, Neptune). Sentence should be about the picture.

_____

- -

_____

- -

_____

- -

_____

Children analyze and respond to literary and informational text.

DIRECTIONS Circle the word that needs a capital letter.

light   sky   (saturn)

Writing

DIRECTIONS Write an introduction for your planet book.

Possible response: Mars is the
fourth planet from the sun.

Children practice various conventions of standard English. Children write routinely for a range of tasks, purposes, and audiences.

Name _____

DIRECTIONS Pick a word from the box to finish each compound word.
Write it on the line. Draw a line to the picture it matches.

| boat | man | paper | watch |

1. news **paper**

2. row **boat**

3. wrist **watch**

4. snow **man**

Find the compound word. Circle the letter.

5. **A.** raining

B. rainy

C. raincoat

6. **A.** popcorn

B. puppy

C. popping

7. **A.** mitten

B. marching

C. backpack

Children apply grade-level phonics and word analysis skills.

Name _____

DIRECTIONS Choose a word from below and draw it in the box. Then write a sentence using the word.

closest   strongest

Responses will vary.

Would you like to walk on the moon? Tell why or why not.

Possible responses: Yes, it would be fun to make footprints on the moon. No, it would be scary to walk in space.

Children demonstrate contextual understanding of Benchmark Vocabulary. Children read text closely and use text evidence in their written answers.

Name _____

DIRECTIONS Circle the word that is spelled incorrectly. Write the word correctly on the line.

Do (yu) see the sun? **you** _____

Writing

DIRECTIONS Write 3 questions that you will answer in your planet book.

Possible responses: What is Mars like? What is the temperature on Mars? Can we live on Mars?

Children practice various conventions of standard English. Children write routinely for a range of tasks, purposes, and audiences.

Name _____

DIRECTIONS Choose a word from below and draw it in the box. Then write a sentence using the word.

tools   study

[ ]

Responses will vary.

Write in Response to Reading

DIRECTIONS Write your answer on the lines.

What does a rover look like?

Possible response: A rover has

wheels. It has cameras.

_____

_____

_____

Children demonstrate contextual understanding of Benchmark Vocabulary. Children read text closely and use text evidence in their written answers.

DIRECTIONS Circle the word that is spelled incorrectly. Write the word.

Mars is (wun) of the planets. **one** _____

DIRECTIONS Write the answer to one of your questions that you can include in your planet book.

Possible response: Mars is cold and cannot support life.

Children practice various conventions of standard English. Children write routinely for a range of tasks, purposes, and audiences.

Name _____

DIRECTIONS Circle the word for each picture.

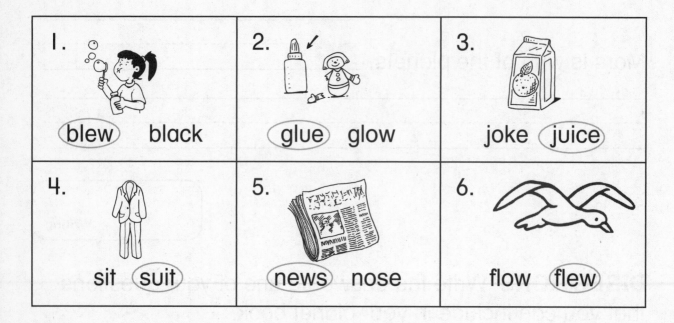

| 1. (blew) black | 2. (glue) glow | 3. joke (juice) |
| 4. sit (suit) | 5. (news) nose | 6. flow (flew) |

Read the words in the box.
Pick a word to finish each sentence.

| bruise | drew | true |

7. It is ____**true**____ that I like grapes.

8. He has a ____**bruise**____ on his leg.

9. My sister ____**drew**____ this picture.

Children apply grade-level phonics and word analysis skills.

Name _____

DIRECTIONS Choose a word from below and draw it in the box. Then write a sentence using the word.

brightly   larger

Responses will vary.

Write in Response to Reading

What is the most interesting fact you learned about the sun?

Possible response: The sun is a burning ball of gases!

Children demonstrate contextual understanding of Benchmark Vocabulary. Children read text closely and use text evidence in their written answers.

Name _____

Finding a Voice

Cam was unhappy. He would be in the hospital for many weeks. He had a tube in his throat. He could not talk. How could he tell his mom or dad that he wanted something? How could he talk with friends?

One day a nurse had an idea. She found a special tool for him to use. Cam's eyes lit up when she gave it to him. The tool looked like a computer keyboard with a screen. Cam typed a word. He typed a sentence. Then he pushed a button. The computer said what Cam typed!

This computer uses special software. It helps people who have difficulty speaking. It gives them a "voice." The software can fit on the tiniest computers. This software has given people freedom to communicate. That's something to shout about!

Children read text closely to determine what the text says.

Name _____

Look for Clues

Circle the sentence that tells how Cam felt **before** he got his computer. Underline clues that show how Cam felt **after** he got the computer.

Look for Clues: Extend Your Ideas

Think about how Cam felt before he got the computer. Box the sentences that tell why Cam felt this way.

Ask Questions

What do you wonder about the special software? Write two questions.

_____

Responses will vary but should relate to text

evidence. Possible responses: Can people type really

long sentences? What does the computer sound like?

Ask Questions: Extend Your Ideas

Suppose you wonder how the special software helps people. Underline the sentences in the text that will answer that question.

Make Your Case

What do you think is the most interesting fact about the software? Box the fact in the text. Responses will vary.

Children read text closely to determine what the text says.

Name _____

DIRECTIONS Add letters to spell words.

_____ed   _____ed   _____ed

Responses should be letters that spell any words with -ed, such as *red, bed, fed*.

DIRECTIONS Write a detail about your planet that you can put in your planet book.

_____

Possible response: Mars is smaller than Earth.

Children practice various conventions of standard English. Children write routinely for a range of tasks, purposes, and audiences.

Name _____

DIRECTIONS Choose a word from below and draw it in the box. Then write a sentence using the word.

center   seasons

Responses will vary.

Write in Response to Reading

What is the most interesting thing you learned from the section called "Planets and the Sun"?

Responses will vary but should include facts or details from this section of the text.

 Children demonstrate contextual understanding of Benchmark Vocabulary. Children read text closely and use text evidence in their written answers.

Name _____

DIRECTIONS Circle the correct word to complete the sentence.

The sun (seems / seem) to move across the sky.

Writing

DIRECTIONS Create a text feature to include in your planet book.

Responses should be a text feature about their planet.

Children practice various conventions of standard English. Children write routinely for a range of tasks, purposes, and audiences.

Name _____

DIRECTIONS Choose a word from below and draw it in the box. Then write a sentence using the word.

spins   rises   sets

Responses will vary.

_____

_____

_____

Write in Response to Reading

Write one thing you learned from the book.

_____

Responses will vary but could include one of the following: the Sun shines brightly; the Sun

_____

is a yellow star; the Sun is the closest star to Earth; the Sun is 93 million miles away from

_____

Earth; the Sun is a burning ball of gases; the Sun is much larger than Earth; the Sun is the

_____

center of the solar system.

 Children demonstrate contextual understanding of Benchmark Vocabulary. Children read text closely and use text evidence in their written answers.

DIRECTIONS Circle the correct word to complete the sentence.

Tomorrow we will (wrote / write) about the planet.

DIRECTIONS Write a conclusion to your planet book.

Possible response: Someday people will visit Mars.

Children practice various conventions of standard English. Children write routinely for a range of tasks, purposes, and audiences.

Name _____

DIRECTIONS Add **-ly** or **-ful** to the word in ( ).
Write the new word on the line.

(play)
_____

1. The dog is _____ **playful** _____ .

(slow)
_____

2. The dog walked _____ **slowly** _____ .

(quick)
_____

3. Then it ran _____ **quickly** _____ !

(safe)
_____

4. The dog got home _____ **safely** _____ .

(thank)
_____

5. Miss Moon was _____ **thankful** _____ .

Children apply grade-level phonics and word
analysis skills.

Name _____

DIRECTIONS Choose a word from below and draw it in the box. Then write a sentence using the word.

hotter   larger

Responses will vary.

Write in Response to Reading

Write a fact that you learned about the sun.

Responses will vary but should include facts about the sun from the text.

Children demonstrate contextual understanding of Benchmark Vocabulary. Children read text closely and use text evidence in their written answers.

Name _____

DIRECTIONS Write one way the two texts are the same.

Responses will vary but should tell how the two texts are alike.

Write one way the two texts are different.

Responses will vary but should tell how the two texts are different.

Children analyze and respond to literary and informational text.

Name _____

DIRECTIONS Find the mistakes in the sentence.
Write the sentence correctly.

earth and venus ar planet

Earth and Venus are planets.

DIRECTIONS Rewrite one sentence from your planet book
with correct capitalization, spelling, and punctuation.

Responses will vary but should
have correct capitalization,
spelling, and punctuation.

Children practice various conventions of standard
English. Children write routinely for a range of tasks,
purposes, and audiences.

Name _____

DIRECTIONS Choose a word from below and draw it in the box. Then write a sentence using the word.

dwarf   center

[drawing box]

Responses will vary.

Write in Response to Reading

What questions do you have after reading about the sun and the planets?

Responses will vary but should be questions.

Children demonstrate contextual understanding of Benchmark Vocabulary. Children read text closely and use text evidence in their written answers.

DIRECTIONS Choose two of the eight big planets.
Draw the two planets.

Write the names of the planets under the drawings.

Responses will vary, but drawings should resemble the two planets named below.	

-- --

Tell how the two planets are the same.
Tell how they are different.

Responses will vary but should
show an understanding of
the characteristics of the two
planets chosen.

Children analyze and respond to literary and
informational text.

Name _____

DIRECTIONS Find the mistakes in the sentence.
Write the sentence correctly.

do you think it's fun to read about the planets

Do you think it's fun to read about the planets?

What do you still need to fix? Write your notes here.

Responses will vary.

Children practice various conventions of
standard English. Children write routinely for a
range of tasks, purposes, and audiences.

Name _____

DIRECTIONS Circle the word for each picture.

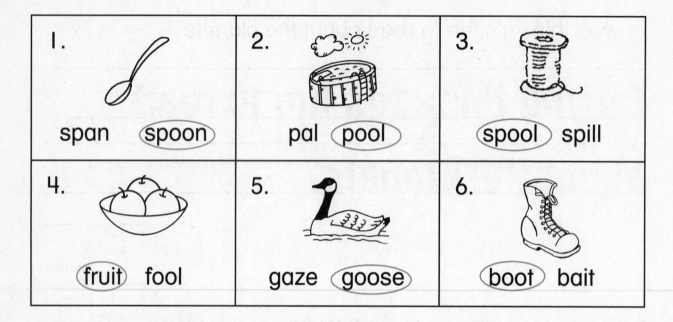

1. span (spoon)

2. pal (pool)

3. (spool) spill

4. (fruit) fool

5. gaze (goose)

6. (boot) bait

Pick a word to finish each sentence.
Write the word in the sentence.

7. The _____**moose**_____ blocked the cars on the road.

    moose   mouse

8. I need a _____**broom**_____ to clean this mess!

    boot   broom

Children apply grade-level phonics and word
analysis skills.

Name _____

DIRECTIONS Pick a word from the box to match each picture. Write it on the line.

| cloud | clown | flower | house |

1. cloud

2. flower

3. house

4. clown

Unscramble the letters to make a word.

uold _____ **loud** _____   wtno _____ **town** _____

Pick a word to finish each sentence. Write it on the line.

5. The radio was too _____ **loud** _____.

6. I like to shop in _____ **town** _____.

Children apply grade-level phonics and word analysis skills.

Unit 6 • Module A • Lesson 1 • 375

Name _____

DIRECTIONS Choose a word from below and draw it in the box. Then write a sentence using the word.

neighborhoods   study   traditional

Responses will vary.

Write in Response to Reading

DIRECTIONS Complete the sentence.

The United States is Possible response:

a nation of many people.

Children demonstrate contextual understanding of Benchmark Vocabulary. Children read text closely and use text evidence in their written answers.

Name _____

DIRECTIONS Combine the two sentences to form a compound sentence.

We played basketball. We had fun.

We played basketball, and we had fun.

Writing

DIRECTIONS Write about the country from the book you would like to visit.

Possible response: I would like to visit Mongolia.

Children practice various conventions of standard English. Children write routinely for a range of tasks, purposes, and audiences.

Name _____

DIRECTIONS Choose a word from below and draw it in the box. Then write a sentence using the word.

peek   prepare   designs

Responses will vary.

Write in Response to Reading

DIRECTIONS Write one sentence that tells a fact about Ama.

Possible response: Ama loves to swim.

Children demonstrate contextual understanding of Benchmark Vocabulary. Children read text closely and use text evidence in their written answers.

Name _____

DIRECTIONS Add details to the sentence. Write the new sentence on the lines.

We eat dinner.

Responses will vary. Sample response: We eat chicken and rice for dinner.

DIRECTIONS Add reasons to support your opinion.

Possible response: I would like to visit Mongolia because the people have horses and give presents to each other.

Children practice various conventions of standard English. Children write routinely for a range of tasks, purposes, and audiences.

Name _____

DIRECTIONS Circle the word for each picture.

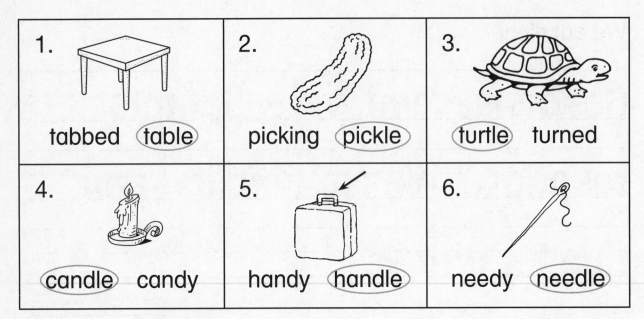

1. tabbed (table)

2. picking (pickle)

3. (turtle) turned

4. (candle) candy

5. handy (handle)

6. needy (needle)

Find the word that has the same ending sound as .
Circle the letter.

7. **A.** litter

 B. lightly

 (C.) little

8. **(A.)** purple

 B. purred

 C. purest

Children apply grade-level phonics and word analysis skills.

Name _____

DIRECTIONS Choose a word from below and draw it in the box. Then write a sentence using the word.

tasty   celebrates   lively

[ ]

Responses will vary.

Write in Response to Reading

What does Raul enjoy about his family?

Raul thinks it's cool to speak English and Spanish.

What does Britta enjoy doing?

Britta enjoys eating pizza and dancing.

 Children demonstrate contextual understanding of Benchmark Vocabulary. Children read text closely and use text evidence in their written answers.

A Horse Named Chester

Did you ever see a horse in a store? Chester goes into stores. Chester is special. He is a service horse. Chester's owner, Mike, cannot see. Chester helps Mike every day. Chester leads him along. He helps Mike cross streets. Chester helps Mike find his way.

Chester looks much like other horses. But he is much smaller. He is the size of a large dog.

People have used service dogs for many years. Some people think horses are better helpers. Small horses like Chester are gentle. They are friendly. They can learn to help people. They can live for 30 years or more.

Trainers teach service horses to do their jobs. Service horses are good helpers. They are also great friends.

Children read text closely to determine what the text says.

Name _____

Look for Clues

Circle the sentence that tells what the writer thinks about service horses.

Ask Questions

Write one question about service horses.

Responses will vary but may include: What jobs can service horses do for people?

Ask Questions: Extend Your Ideas

Underline the sentences in the story that relate to your question. Responses will vary based on the question asked.

Make Your Case

Underline the words in the text that tell what you learned about service horses. Responses will vary.

Make Your Case: Extend Your Ideas

Write what you learned about service horses.

Responses will vary, but children should use evidence from the text, such as service horses are small and friendly.

Children read text closely to determine what the text says.

Name _____

DIRECTIONS Write the date that you were born. Be sure to include commas.

Response should include month, day, and year with comma after day.

Writing

DIRECTIONS Add a sense of closure to your opinion writing from Lessons 1 and 2.

Possible response: Mongolia sounds like a good place to visit.

Children practice various conventions of standard English. Children write routinely for a range of tasks, purposes, and audiences.

Name _____

DIRECTIONS Choose a word from below and draw it in the box. Then write a sentence using the word.

serves several blurs

Responses will vary.

Write in Response to Reading

DIRECTIONS Write your response in complete sentences.

Name 3 things the text mentions about Kenyans.

Possible response: Kenyans eat fish stew. Kenyans eat with their right hands only. Many fast marathon runners are Kenyan.

Children demonstrate contextual understanding of Benchmark Vocabulary. Children read text closely and use text evidence in their written answers.

Name _____

DIRECTIONS Write your name with **'s** and something that belongs to you.

Response should show the possessive form ('s) of the child's name.

DIRECTIONS Write a complete sentence telling your favorite custom in your family.

Responses will vary. Possible response: My favorite custom in my family is eating cake on my birthday.

Children practice various conventions of standard English. Children write routinely for a range of tasks, purposes, and audiences.

Name _____

DIRECTIONS Choose a word from below and draw it in the box. Then write a sentence using the word.

respect   sip   rude

Responses will vary.

Write in Response to Reading

DIRECTIONS Write your answer on the lines. Use a complete sentence.

Why is Suhe still learning to speak English?

Possible response: Suhe did not speak English when he lived in Mongolia.

Children demonstrate contextual understanding of Benchmark Vocabulary. Children read text closely and use text evidence in their written answers.

Name _____

DIRECTIONS Circle the correct word to complete the sentence.

That is (a / an) good poem.

That is (a / an) excellent poem.

Writing

DIRECTIONS Write one or more reasons to support your opinion from Lesson 4.

Possible responses: My mom
bakes a coconut cake. I get to
make a wish.

Children practice various conventions of standard English. Children write routinely for a range of tasks, purposes, and audiences.

Name _____

DIRECTIONS Write a word from the box to match each picture.

| towel | snow | couch | soup |

1.
_____
soup

2.
_____
snow

3.
_____
couch

4.
_____
towel

Write the word to finish each sentence. Remember to use a capital letter at the beginning of a sentence.

5. _____ How _____ does the plant grow? **how   have**

6. I like to _____ blow _____ bubbles. **blue   blow**

7. Can I play at your _____ house _____? **toy   house**

Children apply grade-level phonics and word analysis skills.

Name _____

DIRECTIONS Choose a word from below and draw it in the box. Then write a sentence using the word.

picnic   overcoat

Responses will vary.

Write in Response to Reading

DIRECTIONS Write your answer on the lines. Use complete sentences.

What do you think of Tony's family?

Possible responses: They have

fun. They are happy.

Children demonstrate contextual understanding of Benchmark Vocabulary. Children read text closely and use text evidence in their written answers.

Name _____

DIRECTIONS Write the dates correctly.

july 4 1776 _____ **July 4, 1776**

may 5 2005 _____ **May 5, 2005**

DIRECTIONS Circle the correct word. Then complete the sentence about *A Picnic in October*. Write information from the book that supports your opinion.

I liked / disliked **Responses will vary.**

_____

_____

_____

_____

_____

_____

_____

_____

_____

Children practice various conventions of standard English. Children write routinely for a range of tasks, purposes, and audiences.

Name _____

DIRECTIONS Choose a word from below and draw it in the box. Then write a sentence using the word.

cousins   ferry   island

Responses will vary.

DIRECTIONS Write your answer on the lines.
On page 10, the family gets in line. What are they waiting for?

Possible response: They are waiting to get on a ferry to take them to the Statue of Liberty.

Children demonstrate contextual understanding of Benchmark Vocabulary. Children read text closely and use text evidence in their written answers.

Name _____

DIRECTIONS Read the sentences from *A Picnic in October*. Circle the words that describe something.

She's wearing her (bright) (green) coat.

The wind ruffles the (fake fur) collar (around her neck.)

Across on the island, the Statue of Liberty stands, (white) and (gleaming.)

Mike's holding the cake now, in its (see-through) container.

Write a sentence to describe the people waiting in line on pages 10 and 11.

Responses will vary but could include descriptions of what characters are wearing or what they are doing in the illustration.

Children analyze and respond to literary texts.

Name _____

DIRECTIONS Circle the word that tells who the family belongs to.

(Tony's) family went on a picnic in October.

DIRECTIONS Write an introduction to your book review. Name the book. Tell about the book. Write your opinion.

A Picnic in October by Eve Bunting is about a boy named Tony and his family visiting the Statue of Liberty. I think this book is very good.

Children practice various conventions of standard English. Children write routinely for a range of tasks, purposes, and audiences.

Name _____

DIRECTIONS Circle the word for each picture.

1. lesson (lemon)	2. (bacon) basket	3. came (camel)
4. (cabin) cab	5. timber (tiger)	6. (river) rigged

Draw a picture for each word.

7. spider

Drawings will vary.

8. baby

Drawings will vary.

Children apply grade-level phonics and word analysis skills.

Name _____

DIRECTIONS Choose a word from below and draw it in the box. Then write a sentence using the word.

understand   disapproving

[box]

_____

Responses will vary.

DIRECTIONS Read page 13 in *A Picnic in October*. Why does the woman feel better at the end of the page?

_____

Possible response: She

understands that the ferry is

coming back.

_____

Children demonstrate contextual understanding of Benchmark Vocabulary. Children read text closely and use text evidence in their written answers.

Name _____

DIRECTIONS Look at pages 12 through 14 of *A Picnic in October*. Write one detail about a character on these pages.

Responses will vary but should show evidence from these pages in the text.

Write one detail about the events on these pages.

Responses will vary but should show evidence from these pages in the text.

Children analyze and respond to literary text.

Name _____

DIRECTIONS Write the two sentences as one sentence. Then add a detail.

We went on a picnic. It was fun.

Possible response: We went on a picnic to the park, and it was fun.

DIRECTIONS Write at least one reason to support your opinion for your book report.

Possible responses: I enjoyed the book because the family is nice to each other. The text says that "Grandpa can be really soppy."

Children practice various conventions of standard English. Children write routinely for a range of tasks, purposes, and audiences.

Name _____

DIRECTIONS Choose a word from below and draw it in the box. Then write a sentence using the word.

entered   offended

Responses will vary.

Write in Response to Reading

DIRECTIONS Complete the sentence.

I would like to go to Liberty Island because Possible

response: the Statue of Liberty is

there.

Children demonstrate contextual understanding of Benchmark Vocabulary. Children read text closely and use text evidence in their written answers.

Name _____

DIRECTIONS Circle the word in ( ) to complete the sentence.

(This / Those) park is a good place for a picnic.

Writing

DIRECTIONS Write an ending to your writing from Lessons 7 and 8. Be sure to restate your opinion.

<u>Possible responses: A Picnic in</u>

<u>October is a good book because</u>

<u>the grandmother teaches her</u>

<u>family to be proud of America.</u>

Children practice various conventions of standard English. Children write routinely for a range of tasks, purposes, and audiences.

Name _____

DIRECTIONS Choose a word from below and draw it in the box. Then write a sentence using the word.

gazes   barrier

Responses will vary.

Write in Response to Reading

DIRECTIONS Complete the sentence.

I think Lady Liberty is Possible responses:

interesting, neat, inspiring, important.

Children demonstrate contextual understanding of Benchmark Vocabulary. Children read text closely and use text evidence in their written answers.

Name _____

DIRECTIONS Write the two sentences as one sentence. Then add a detail.

A band played. We listened to music.

Possible response: A band played on stage, and we listened to good music.

DIRECTIONS Add more details or combine sentences in your writing. Write the new sentence below.

A Picnic in October is about a family going to see the Statue of Liberty where they will have a picnic.

Children practice various conventions of standard English. Children write routinely for a range of tasks, purposes, and audiences.

Name _____

DIRECTIONS Circle the word for each picture.

1. had (hood)	2. (cook) coat	3. bake (book)
4. wide (wood)	5. store (stood)	6. (hook) hard

Read the words in the box.
Circle the words that have the same vowel sound as .
Pick one of these words to finish each sentence.

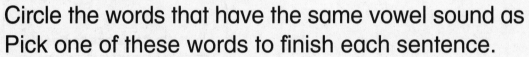

take (foot) (took) soon goat tool (good)

7. He __**took**__ a picture.

8. That was a __**good**__ joke.

9. My __**foot**__ hurts.

Children apply grade-level phonics and
word analysis skills.

Name _____

DIRECTIONS Choose a word from below and draw it in the box. Then write a sentence using the word.

staring   respectful

Responses will vary.

Write in Response to Reading

DIRECTIONS Write your answer on the lines.

What does Tony do at the end of the story?

He wishes the Statue of Liberty

a happy birthday.

Children demonstrate contextual understanding of Benchmark Vocabulary. Children read text closely and use text evidence in their written answers.

Name _____

What is the central message of *A Picnic in October?*

Responses will vary but could include that the Statue of Liberty stands for freedom to many people.

Retell three details that show that message.

1. **Possible response: Tony's family has a picnic to celebrate the Statue of Liberty's birthday.**

2. **Possible response: Tony sees another family also celebrating the Statue's birthday.**

3. **Possible response: Tony finally understands why the Statue of Liberty is so important to Grandma.**

Children analyze and respond to literary text.

Name _____

DIRECTIONS Find the mistake. Write the sentence correctly.

Grandpas hat is black.

_____

Grandpa's hat is black.

DIRECTIONS Add a detail to your book report using a peer's suggestion.

_____

Possible response: Tony is a

nice person because he helps

a woman who doesn't speak

English.

_____

_____

_____

Children practice various conventions of standard English. Children write routinely for a range of tasks, purposes, and audiences.

Name _____

DIRECTIONS Choose a word from below and draw it in the box. Then write a sentence using the word.

traditional   celebrates   island

Responses will vary.

Write in Response to Reading

DIRECTIONS Write your answer on the lines.

What traditions can Ama, Raul, and Tony teach each other?

Ama can teach about the Cherokee National Holiday and Cherokee marbles. Raul can

teach about Mexican Independence Day. Tony can teach about his family's picnic in

October.

Children demonstrate contextual understanding of Benchmark Vocabulary. Children read text closely and use text evidence in their written answers.

DIRECTIONS Find the mistakes.
Write the sentence correctly.

We stand in lin to tak the ferry.

We stand in line to take the
ferry.

Writing

DIRECTIONS Read your book review. Look for any mistakes in spelling, capital letters, or end punctuation.

Put a check mark in each box to show you have checked for mistakes in your review.

❑ I checked the spelling of every word.

❑ I checked that the author's name is spelled correctly.

❑ I wrote the title of the book correctly.

❑ I used a capital letter at the beginning of each sentence.

❑ I used a capital letter at the beginning of each name.

❑ I capitalized the word *I* every time I used it.

❑ I put an end mark at the end of each sentence.

Children practice various conventions of standard English. Children write routinely for a range of tasks, purposes, and audiences.

Name _____

DIRECTIONS Add **-s**, **-ed**, or **-ing** to the word in ( ).
Write the new word on the line.

(hope + -s)

1. Jean _____ **hopes** _____ to grow corn.

(slope + -ing)

2. She plants seeds on the _____ **sloping** _____ hill.

(care + -ed)

3. Jean _____ **cared** _____ for the plants.

(taste + -ed)

4. Jean _____ **tasted** _____ the corn.

(smile + -ing)

5. She is _____ **smiling** _____ .

Children apply grade-level phonics and word
analysis skills.

Name _____

DIRECTIONS Choose a word from below and draw it in the box. Then write a sentence using the word.

study   gazes

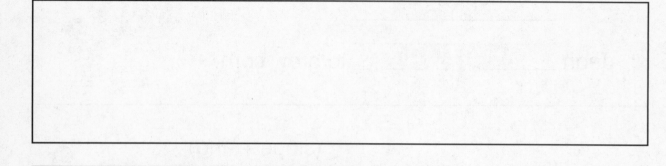

Responses will vary.

Write in Response to Reading

DIRECTIONS Write your answer on the lines.

What would Tony tell Mr. Tucker's class about his family?

Responses will vary but should tell about Tony and his family visiting the Statue of Liberty.

Children demonstrate contextual understanding of Benchmark Vocabulary. Children read text closely and use text evidence in their written answers.

Name _____

Welcome to Pilsen

Pilsen is part of Chicago. It has a rich history. People from many parts of the world live in Pilsen. In the 1950s, many people from Mexico began to move here. They came to find work. They came to help their families. They brought their favorite music and foods. They brought their traditions. They also brought their love of art!

The Mexican American community has created beautiful murals. A mural is a large painting on a wall. You can see these murals on schools and churches. They are on bridges and in parks. You can even see them on apartment buildings and houses. Pilsen is a work of art!

Many of the murals show important ideas. They show Mexican history and heroes. You see pictures of people working hard. One mural shows a family cooking a meal. Mexican culture is alive and well in Pilsen!

Children read text closely to determine what the text says.

Name _____

Look for Clues
Underline three details that tell what the murals show.

Ask Questions
Write one question you would like to ask an artist in Pilsen.

Possible response: How long does it take you to paint one

mural?

Make Your Case
Circle feeling words that help you understand how the author feels about Pilsen. Then write how the author feels.

Responses will vary but should include the author's feelings

of pride in Pilsen's history, music, art, food, and people.

Make Your Case: Extend Your Ideas
Why is Pilsen a special place? Use details from the passage.

Responses will vary but should include details about its

diversity and proud history as well as the beauty of the

murals.

Children read text closely to determine what the text says.

Name _____

DIRECTIONS Fill in the missing word.

_____

Looking at ____the____ Statue of Liberty makes me proud.

DIRECTIONS Write a title for your book review.

Possible response: *A Picnic in October* Has a Place in My Heart

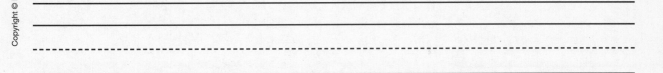 Children practice various conventions of standard English. Children write routinely for a range of tasks, purposes, and audiences.

Phonics

DIRECTIONS Circle the word for each picture.

1. coins canes

2. bay boy

3. boil bail

4. joy jay

5. foil fail

6. round royal

Pick a word to finish each sentence.
Write the word on the line.

7. May I _____join_____ you?   (jolly, join)

8. My new _____toy_____ is that doll.   (tray, toy)

Children apply grade-level phonics and word analysis skills.

Name _____

DIRECTIONS Choose a word from below and draw it in the box. Then write a sentence using the word.

fair   booths   explore

Responses will vary.

Write in Response to Reading

DIRECTIONS Draw a picture of one of the stands at the fair. Write a sentence to tell about the stand.

Drawings should show one of the stands from *Whose Is This?*

Responses will vary.

Children demonstrate contextual understanding of Benchmark Vocabulary. Children read text closely and use text evidence in their written answers.

Name _____

DIRECTIONS Circle the correct word.

Look at all (this / (these)) people!

Where should we put ((this) / these) box?

DIRECTIONS Name the topic. Then write your opinion about the topic.

Responses will vary.

Children practice various conventions of standard English. Children write routinely for a range of tasks, purposes, and audiences.

Name _____

DIRECTIONS Choose a word from below and draw it in the box. Then write a sentence using the word.

delicious   peered   mischief

Responses will vary.

DIRECTIONS Write your answer on the lines.

What is a culture fair?

Responses will vary but should include that people share their cultures with others.

Children demonstrate contextual understanding of Benchmark Vocabulary. Children read text closely and use text evidence in their written answers.

Name _____

DIRECTIONS Circle the correct word.

That was (the / a) best movie I ever saw!

I just read (the / a) book about plants.

Writing

DIRECTIONS Think about your opinion from Lesson 1.
Write to tell why you feel this way.

Responses will vary.

Children practice various conventions of standard
English. Children write routinely for a range of tasks,
purposes, and audiences.

Name _____

DIRECTIONS Write a word from the box to match each picture.

| baker | sailor | painter | teacher |

1.

   painter

2.

   sailor

3.

   baker

4.

   teacher

Draw a picture of each word.

5. driver

6. actor

Pictures will vary.

Children apply grade-level phonics and word analysis skills.

Name _____

DIRECTIONS Choose a word from below and draw it in the box. Then write a sentence using the word.

objects   cloth   clues

Responses will vary.

Write in Response to Reading

DIRECTIONS Draw a picture to show what Kimi pulls from the box. Write a sentence that tells about the object.

Drawings should show a long, orange piece of cloth.

Responses will vary but should include details from the story.

Children demonstrate contextual understanding of Benchmark Vocabulary. Children read text closely and use text evidence in their written answers.

Name _____

DIRECTIONS Choose a word from the story. Write the word. Then write your responses on the lines.

_____

Word: Responses will vary.

What is the meaning of the word?

Responses will vary.

_____

Write a sentence that uses the word to tell about something in real life.

Responses will vary.

_____

Children analyze and respond to literary texts.

Name _____

DIRECTIONS Write these two sentences as one sentence.

It's summer! I'm so happy!

It's summer, and I'm so happy!

DIRECTIONS Write about activities at the culture fair. Circle the activity you would enjoy the most.

Responses will vary.

Children practice various conventions of standard English. Children write routinely for a range of tasks, purposes, and audiences.

Name _____

DIRECTIONS Choose a word from below and draw it in the box. Then write a sentence using the word.

puzzled   competition

Responses will vary.

Write in Response to Reading

DIRECTIONS Draw a picture of something a person from India might wear. Write a sentence to tell about your picture.

Drawings should show a sari, bangles, a bindi, or a turban.

Responses will vary.

Children demonstrate contextual understanding of Benchmark Vocabulary. Children read text closely and use text evidence in their written answers.

Name _____

DIRECTIONS Write today's date.

month, date, and year with

comma after date

DIRECTIONS Look for details that support your opinion.
Write the details and where you found them.

Responses will vary.

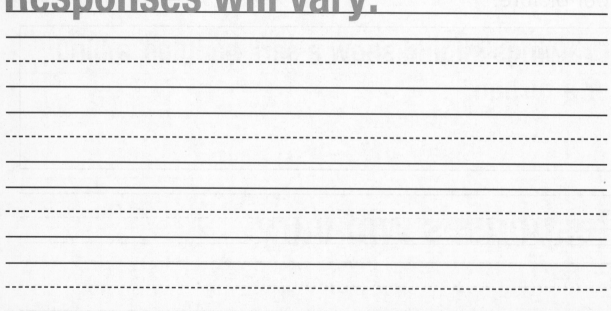 Children practice various conventions of standard
English. Children write routinely for a range of tasks,
purposes, and audiences.

Name _____

DIRECTIONS Choose a word from below and draw it in the box. Then write a sentence using the word.

behind   spotted   meetings

Responses will vary.

Write in Response to Reading

DIRECTIONS Draw a picture of the object Maria pulls from the box. Then write a sentence about the object.

Drawings should show the talking stick.

Responses will vary but should include details from the story.

Children demonstrate contextual understanding of Benchmark Vocabulary. Children read text closely and use text evidence in their written answers.

DIRECTIONS Think about what happens in this part of the story. Draw the events in order.

Drawings will vary but should show the events in this part of the story.

Children analyze and respond to literary texts.

Name _____

DIRECTIONS Write the correct word: **and or but.**

_____

Do you want a dog, _____ **or** _____ do you want a cat?

DIRECTIONS Begin writing your opinion piece.

Responses will vary.

Children practice various conventions of standard English. Children write routinely for a range of tasks, purposes, and audiences.

Name _____

DIRECTIONS Circle the word for each picture.

1. pail (paw)

2. (yawn) yard

3. stray (straw)

4. face (faucet)

5. (auto) ace

6. lane (lawn)

Pick a word to finish each sentence. Circle the word. Write the word in the sentence.

7. I like to eat red _____sauce_____.

   (sauce)   sash

8. The bear uses its _____claw_____ to catch fish.

   clay   (claw)

Children apply grade-level phonics and word analysis skills.

Name _____

DIRECTIONS Choose a word from below and draw it in the box. Then write a sentence using the word.

shiny   polished   hollows

[drawing box]

Responses will vary.

Write in Response to Reading

DIRECTIONS Complete the sentence.

One thing Maria and Kimi pull out of the box is

Responses will vary but should include either the wooden case or the metal object.

Children demonstrate contextual understanding of Benchmark Vocabulary. Children read text closely and use text evidence in their written answers.

Name _____

DIRECTIONS Write the correct word: **so** **because.**

I was tired, _____**so**_____ I took a nap.

DIRECTIONS Write at least one reason for your opinion.

Responses will vary.

Children practice various conventions of standard English. Children write routinely for a range of tasks, purposes, and audiences.

Name _____

Benchmark Vocabulary

DIRECTIONS Choose a word from below and draw it in the box. Then write a sentence using the word.

peeped   handle   detectives

Responses will vary.

Write in Response to Reading

DIRECTIONS Draw a picture that shows how the story ends. Then write a sentence to tell about the ending.

Drawings will vary.

Responses will vary but should tell about the story ending.

 Children demonstrate contextual understanding of Benchmark Vocabulary. Children read text closely and use text evidence in their written answers.

Name _____

DIRECTIONS Circle the words that tell where something is.

The paper is (on the desk.)

The trees (in the park) are so big!

DIRECTIONS Write an ending for your opinion piece.

Responses will vary.

Children practice various conventions of standard English. Children write routinely for a range of tasks, purposes, and audiences.

Name _____

DIRECTIONS Circle the word that names each picture.

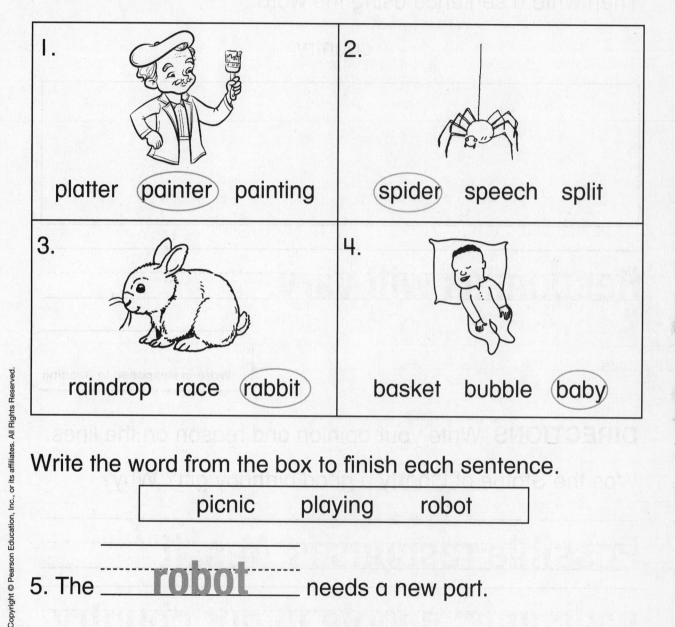

1. platter (painter) painting

2. (spider) speech split

3. raindrop race (rabbit)

4. basket bubble (baby)

Write the word from the box to finish each sentence.

picnic	playing	robot

5. The _____**robot**_____ needs a new part.

6. Let's have a _____**picnic**_____ at the park.

7. What game are you _____**playing**_____?

Children apply grade-level phonics and word analysis skills.

Name _____

Benchmark Vocabulary

DIRECTIONS Draw a picture of the word below in the box. Then write a sentence using the word.

country

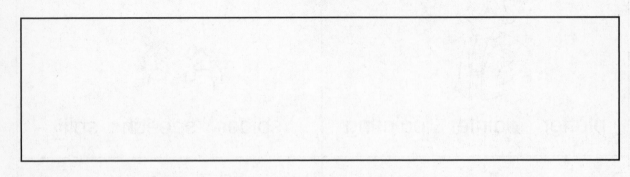

Responses will vary.

Write in Response to Reading

DIRECTIONS Write your opinion and reason on the lines.

Was the Statue of Liberty a good birthday gift? Why?

Possible responses: Yes, it welcomes people to our country. No, it was too big and had to be put together.

Children demonstrate contextual understanding of Benchmark Vocabulary. Children read text closely and use text evidence in their written answers.

Name _____

The Festival

My school had a world festival. I think every school should have one. We celebrated different countries and cultures around the world. The best part was the music. I liked dancing to the music, too. I even played music!

My friend Jose is from Puerto Rico. He shared neat things about his homeland. People speak Spanish there. They eat fruits like guava and mango. They dance to salsa music. Jose let me try the maracas. I like the sound they make when they shake.

I learned about other places around the world at the festival. I heard different languages. I saw instruments that made different sounds. I ate food that was new to me.

I know that people are different. People come from different places around the world. We all live in America. Being different makes our country strong. It makes it special.

Children read text closely to determine what the text says.

Look for Clues

Underline the sentence that tells why the writer thinks every school should have a world festival.

Look for Clues: Extend Your Ideas

In the writer's opinion, what was the best part of the festival? Circle the sentence. Draw a box around the writer's reasons for this opinion.

Ask Questions

What questions would you ask the writer about the world festival?

Responses will vary but should relate to the text.

Ask Questions: Extend Your Ideas

Suppose you wonder what the writer learned about Puerto Rico. Underline the sentences that answer that question.

Make Your Case

What event at this world festival would you enjoy? Underline the event or activity in the third paragraph. Then write reasons from the text to tell why.

Responses will vary but should include text evidence.

Children read text closely to determine what the text says.

Name _____

DIRECTIONS Finish the sentence.

I like to play games and <u>Responses may expand on the</u>

<u>simple sentence or create a compound sentence.</u>

Writing

DIRECTIONS Think about details you can add to your writing. Rewrite your opinion piece.

Responses will vary.

Children practice various conventions of standard English. Children write routinely for a range of tasks, purposes, and audiences.

Name _____

DIRECTIONS Draw a picture of the word below in the box. Then write a sentence using the word.

believe

[ ]

Responses will vary.

Write in Response to Reading

DIRECTIONS Write your answer on the lines.

What does the Statue of Liberty stand for?

Possible response: The statue

stands for freedom.

_____

_____

_____

Children demonstrate contextual understanding of Benchmark Vocabulary. Children read text closely and use text evidence in their written answers.

Name _____

DIRECTIONS Add an end mark to each sentence.

What is our country's birthday?

It is the Fourth of July.

DIRECTIONS Write to tell how you will publish your opinion piece.

Responses will vary.

_____

_____

_____

_____

_____

_____

_____

_____

Children practice various conventions of standard English. Children write routinely for a range of tasks, purposes, and audiences.

Name _____

DIRECTIONS Choose a word from below and draw it in the box. Then write a sentence using the word.

puzzle   hope

Responses will vary.

Write in Response to Reading

DIRECTIONS Write your opinion and reason on the lines.

Which do you think is a better symbol for America: the American flag or the Statue of Liberty? Why?

Possible response: The Statue of Liberty is better because it welcomes people to America.

Children demonstrate contextual understanding of Benchmark Vocabulary. Children read text closely and use text evidence in their written answers.

Name _____

DIRECTIONS Circle the words that need an uppercase letter.

(new york city) has parades every year on (july) 4.

DIRECTIONS Name the topic. Then write your opinion about the topic.

Responses will vary.

Children practice various conventions of standard English. Children write routinely for a range of tasks, purposes, and audiences.

Name _____

DIRECTIONS Add **re-** or **un-** to the word in ( ).
Write the new word on the line.

(build)
_____

1. Mr. Ford will ____ **rebuild** ____ the car.

(happy)
_____

2. He is ____ **unhappy** ____ with the color.

(paint)
_____

3. He will ____ **repaint** ____ it.

(fills)
_____

4. He ____ **refills** ____ the car with gas.

(lock)
_____

5. Don't forget to ____ **unlock** ____ the door!

Children apply grade-level phonics and word analysis skills.

DIRECTIONS Choose a word from below and draw it in the box. Then write a sentence using the word.

cloth   competition   believe

[box]

Responses will vary.

Write in Response to Reading

DIRECTIONS Think about what you learned in *Whose Is This?* and *L Is for Liberty*. Write your answer on the lines.

What can you tell about the people who live in America?

Responses will vary but could include that they come from all different places in the world.

 Children demonstrate contextual understanding of Benchmark Vocabulary. Children read text closely and use text evidence in their written answers.

DIRECTIONS Write to tell how *Whose Is This?* and *L Is for Liberty* are different.

Responses will vary but should include that *Whose Is This?* is a made up story and *L Is for Liberty* has facts and details about a topic.

Children analyze and respond to literary and informational texts.

DIRECTIONS Write the sentence again. Use pronouns for the underlined words.

<u>The immigrants</u> thought <u>the Statue of Liberty</u> was a welcome sight.

They thought it/she was a welcome sight.

DIRECTIONS Write reasons for your opinion.

Responses will vary.

Children practice various conventions of standard English. Children write routinely for a range of tasks, purposes, and audiences.

Name _____

DIRECTIONS Choose a word from below and draw it in the box. Then write a sentence using the word.

peered   hope

Responses will vary.

Write in Response to Reading

DIRECTIONS Think about what you learned in *Whose Is This?* and *L Is for Liberty*. Write your answer on the lines.

What is one thing you learned about immigrants?

_____

Responses will vary but could include that immigrants come to America to be free;

immigrants come from many different countries.

Children demonstrate contextual understanding of Benchmark Vocabulary. Children read text closely and use text evidence in their written answers.

Name _____

Choose a word or phrase from *Whose Is This?* Write it on the line.

Responses will vary.

What is the meaning of the word or phrase?

Responses will vary.

Write a sentence that uses the word or phrase.

Responses will vary.

Choose a word or phrase from *L Is for Liberty*. Write it on the line.

Responses will vary.

What is the meaning of the word or phrase?

Responses will vary.

Write a sentence that uses the word or phrase.

Responses will vary.

Children analyze and respond to literary and informational texts.

Name _____

DIRECTIONS Add **un** or **re**. Then write the meaning of the word.

_____

_____ tie

"do the

opposite of tie" or "tie again"

Add **ful** or **less**. Then write the meaning of the word.

_____

color _____

"full of color" or "without color"

Writing

DIRECTIONS Write an ending for your opinion piece.

Responses will vary.

Children practice various conventions of standard English. Children write routinely for a range of tasks, purposes, and audiences.

Name _____

DIRECTIONS Circle the word for each picture.

1. gold good

2. child chilled

3. past post

4. fin find

5. wind went

6. old all

Circle the word to finish each sentence.

7. I told / tied my baby sister a story.

8. I can't fine / find my pencil.

Children apply grade-level phonics and word analysis skills.